Table of Contents

Introduction

Direct Teaching of Spelling

Regardless of the reading philosophy or program used in a school, all students benefit by direct teaching of spelling. This instruction may be a block of time set aside strictly for spelling instruction or an integrated part of a whole language program.

Students need to be taught:

- how to spell words that are created using English phonemes, as well as common nonphonetic words.
- learning strategies to help them spell difficult words.
- that correct spelling increases their ability to communicate their ideas and feelings to others.

Using This Book

The 30 spelling units contain these components:

- a reproducible list of 15 spelling words
- three sentences for dictation
- four reproducible activity pages for practicing the spelling list words.

A reproducible testing sheet is included on page 146. It contains lines for the 15 spelling words, two special words you may have assigned, three dictation sentences, and three lines that can be used to give review words of your choice from preceding lists.

These components may be placed in a special spelling folder with the student's record sheet *(see page 145)* attached and used as a working portfolio.

Detailed information on each component is given on pages 5 and 6.

The spelling lists can be used for whole-class, small group, or individual instruction. However lessons are used, start where the students are. Some third graders may need to start with a partial list of words. Some fourth graders may be ready to skip over the beginning spelling units. (Spelling Grades 1-2 [EMC 725] or Spelling Grades 5-6 [EMC 727] may be more appropriate for some of your students.)

Following Student Progress

The table of contents contains the skills covered in these spelling lessons. Class and individual record forms (pages 144 and 145) are provided to help you track student progress.

Create Your Own Activities for Spelling Lists

Use the blank forms (pages 147-149) to create spelling lists, configuration puzzles, and word sorts with words from units of study, special holiday words, or words containing a specific phonetic element or skill needing further practice. These forms may also be used to create student-selected spelling lists.

Spelling Unit Components

Lists of Words *(pages 11-20)*
Reproduce the spelling list twice for each student: one copy to use at school and one copy to take home along with the parent letter (page 150).

Students use the list at school for "partner practice" (see page 7), independent practice, and to copy into individual spelling dictionaries (see page 8).

Sentences for Dictation *(pages 21-23)*
There are three dictation sentences for each spelling list. Space for sentence dictation is provided on the test form (see page 146).

Ask students to listen to the complete sentence as you read it. They then repeat it aloud. Give the sentence in phrases, repeating each phrase one time clearly. Have students repeat the phrase. Wait as students write the phrase.

Repeat with each phrase in the sentence. When the whole sentence has been written, read it again having students touch each word as you say it.

Shorten any sentences you feel are too long or difficult for your students.

Activity Pages
Four reproducible pages are provided for each spelling list. These can be used as teacher-directed lessons, for partner practice, or as individual assignments.

Read, Write, & Spell
This page is used for the initial practice of each spelling word. The student spells one word at a time following these steps:

Step 1 - Read the word and spell it aloud.
Step 2 - Copy the word onto the first blank line and spell it again.
Step 3 - Fold the paper along the fold line to cover the spelling words. (Only the last blank line should be seen.) Write the word from memory.
Step 4 - Open the paper and check the spelling. (This is a <u>very</u> important step. Children need to learn to self-correct so that misspellings are not being practiced.) Repeat the steps for each spelling word.

You may want to write the directions for activity 1 on a chart to post in the classroom.

1. Trace and Spell
2. Copy and Spell
3. Cover and Spell
4. Uncover and Check

This page contains two activities that may be done in one or two sessions.

 Visual Memory

Various types of activities are provided to encourage students to think about what the spelling words look like. These include:

- configuration puzzles
- letters to unscramble to make words
- fill in missing letters
- words with word parts to match
- word searches

(Page 148 contains a form for creating your own configuration puzzles for students needing more of this type of practice.)

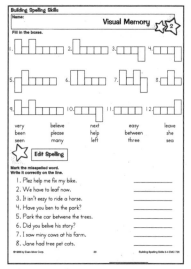

Editing for Correct Spelling

Students identify and correct misspelled words in isolation, in sentences, and in short paragraphs.

 Word Meaning

Students show an understanding of word meaning by filling in missing words, answering questions, or completing crossword puzzles. Practice includes using compound words, words with multiple meanings, contractions, and homonyms.

 Word Study

The phonetic and word analysis skills on this page may be used for direct-teaching lessons or as independent practice.

Phonics

Students fill in missing phonemes and sort words by sound or spelling patterns.

Word Structure

Practice is provided in using word families (rhyming words), contractions, compound words, syllables, and adding suffixes.

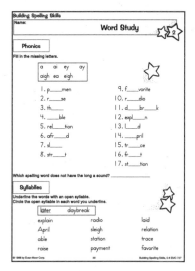

More Ideas for Spelling Practice

Practice with Teacher

Give a pretest to see what type of errors are being made by students. Explain that this is a way to learn what needs to be practiced. It is not a "test" that will be graded in any way. Write each word on a chart or overhead transparency and have students correct their own papers so they can see where they need practice.

Use these errors as a guide for the development of mini-lessons on specific skills or phonemes.

Practice with a Partner

Have students work in pairs to practice their spelling lists. One student gives the word aloud, pronouncing it carefully. The other student writes the word. The "tester" then spells the word aloud as the "writer" checks to see if the word was spelled correctly. Any word missed is written correctly before continuing. After the list is completed, students change roles and repeat the activity.

Extending Use of Spelling Words

1. Have students use the words on their spelling lists in their own writings, both in isolated sentences and in stories and reports.

2. Have students find their spelling words in other places such as posters and charts in the classroom, in literature books, and in magazines or newspapers.

3. Encourage students to find other words that contain the same sound or pattern being studied in the spelling lesson.

Create a Word-Rich Room Environment

You can improve students' spelling by providing a room filled with words.

Provide opportunities for hearing language (talk, tell stories, read to them) and for seeing words (post banners, charts, list of words, student writings; provide literature books, nonfiction books, magazines, etc.).

Write! Write! Write!

Student's writings serve two purposes. They give the student a chance to use the language and spelling skills being learned. They provide the teacher with clues to the student's understanding of sound/letter relationships and can help identify which phonetic elements and structural forms need to be practiced.

You will begin to see fewer spelling errors as students transfer new phonetic or structural understandings from the spelling lessons into their writing experiences.

Student Spelling Dictionaries

Self-made spelling dictionaries provide students with a reference for the spelling of words they frequently use in their writing.

Materials to Use:
- copy of "My Own Spelling Dictionary" form (page 9)
- 26 sheets lined writing paper
- 2 sheets construction paper or tagboard for cover - same size as the writing paper
- stapler
- masking tape

Steps to Follow:
1. Color the cover sheet form. Glue it to the front cover of the dictionary.

2. Staple the lined paper inside the cover. Place masking tape over the staples.

3. Write a letter of the alphabet on each page.

What to Include:
1. When students ask for the correct spelling of a special word, have them write it in their dictionary.

2. Include special words being learned as part of science or social studies units.

3. Include words for special holidays.

4. Include words students continue to misspell on tests and in daily written work.

My Own Spelling Dictionary

_____
My Name

Spelling Strategies

Learning a few simple strategies can help students become better spellers. Teach the strategies one at a time using appropriate words from the spelling lists. List each strategy on a chart as it is introduced. Post the chart as a helpful reminder to students. Review the strategies frequently to help students internalize them.

Say a word correctly.	Don't leave out or mispronounce sounds. Write the sounds in the correct order.
Think about what the word looks like.	Think about how the spelling pattern looks. Write it, look at it, decide if it looks correct.
Look for small words in spelling words.	spin - pin, in cupcake - cup, cake
Look at syllables in spelling words.	Spell the word one syllable at a time. remember - re•mem•ber
Use rhyming words to help spell a word.	If you can spell book, you can spell look.
Use rules for adding endings.	Drop silent e before adding suffix. Double the final consonant before adding suffix. Change the final y to i and add es.
Use knowledge of suffixes and prefixes.	Think about what the word looks like without the prefix or suffix. Write the word and then add the prefix or suffix.
Think about what the word means.	Some words sound the same, but have different meanings and are spelled in different ways. Match the spelling with its meaning.
Use outside help.	Use words posted around the classroom. Use a dictionary. Ask someone for help.

said	next	pitch
ask	left	drink
stand	help	swim
catch	please	life
eight	believe	while
afraid	many	I
away	very	my
always	been	light
playing	seen	buy
waved	she	eye
takes	between	which
than	three	find
great	easy	why
they	sea	kind
prey	leave	try

Building Spelling Skills 3-4 EMC 726

Name:  4	Name:  5	Name:  6
rocket	under	save
pocket	such	give
hold	much	have
told	young	live
often	touch	move
grow	use	above
throne	your	alive
so	you	alike
sew	unit	to
most	cute	two
almost	few	too
both	new	know
coach	fuel	do
open	human	blew
also	music	blue

Building Spelling Skills 3-4 EMC 726

Name:  7	Name:  8	Name:  9
missed	swimming	way
willing	swam	these
balloon	getting	niece
spelling	coming	might
pretty	came	show
still	having	float
off	doing	brain
added	ended	mean
letter	happened	close
different	happening	tried
pattern	started	cube
middle	joked	uniform
Mississippi	received	stayed
zipper	smiled	price
carry	smiling	usually

Building Spelling Skills 3-4 EMC 726

children	into	awful
search	today	called
teacher	without	falling
reached	something	mall
think	become	small
together	upon	straw
with	myself	drawing
where	everybody	strongest
everywhere	everyone	longer
short	maybe	song
push	outside	along
finish	basketball	bought
sure	homework	brought
who	skateboard	rough
whole	earthquake	tough

Building Spelling Skills 3-4 EMC 726

lady
ladies
surprise
surprises
toys
shoes
shy
cry
cried
study
studied
story
only
finally
family

looked
good
brook
football
cookie
stood
full
put
food
school
truth
room
true
chew
due

pointing
oily
boy
voice
oyster
voyage
loyal
joined
coin
choice
poison
destroy
enjoy
choose
chocolate

Building Spelling Skills 3-4 EMC 726

don't

didn't

I'll

I'm

it's

let's

they're

we're

doesn't

o'clock

won't

wouldn't

its

can't

that's

follow

below

own

grown

town

ground

around

found

about

house

group

would

should

country

cousin

April

babies

over

hello

even

we

silent

tiny

menu

future

dear

raise

white

used

those

disagree

again

given

other

money

problem

does

of

some

laid

change

tired

read

nice

lower

city

cereal

face

could

guess

huge

age

danger

goose

gone

coast

clean

guard

giant

carton

word

work

world

were

first

girl

turned

learn

bird

fire

here

nurse

jury

stirred

wear

Name: 22

aren't

partner

hard

chart

farm

start

large

more

before

horse

north

morning

care

stare

warning

Name: 23

threw

through

thoughtless

caught

fault

taught

because

one

once

water

watch

wanted

wonder

wonderful

walk

Name: 24

color

odor

store

calendar

dollar

party

liar

after

number

better

doctor

weather

every

forty

sugar

Building Spelling Skills 3-4 EMC 726

phone

photograph

orphan

alphabet

graph

nephew

enough

father

half

Friday

cough

unhappy

happier

happily

happiness

ghost

neighbor

high

knew

knot

unknown

rewrap

wrong

written

wrapper

unwrap

climb

limb

gnaw

gnat

useful

quietly

slowly

careful

careless

quickly

useless

worthless

fearful

fearless

joyful

smarter

fastest

funniest

happiest

brother	war	air
mother	word	against
another	their	all right
field	there	until
friend	night	presents
heard	knight	beautiful
early	right	favorite
friendly	write	clothes
head	weight	people
near	wait	vacation
year	piece	remember
shield	peace	already
eat	hour	hospital
measure	our	minute
break	wrote	straight

Building Spelling Skills 3-4 EMC 726

Sentences for Dictation

List 1

1. I **asked** my dad to **play catch**.
2. Were **they always playing** that **great** game?
3. Jay is **afraid** of things with **eight** legs.

List 2

1. Has she **seen** the **sea very many** times?
2. I **believe** I **left** my lunch **between** those seats.
3. **Please leave** the **three** books **next** to my desk.

List 3

1. Did you **find** the **kind** of drink you need to **buy**?
2. Don't **swim while** the shark is close by.
3. **Why** did you shine that **light** in **my eye**?

List 4

1. Will your **pocket hold most** of the toy **rockets**?
2. The king **often** sat on his gold **throne**.
3. The **coach** let **almost** all of us play in **both** games.

List 5

1. **Touch** the **cute, young** kitten **under** its chin.
2. Carlos invented a **new fuel** for **humans** to **use**.
3. **Your music** is **such** a treat to hear.

List 6

1. **Save** me that fish until I have **two** dollars.
2. The wind **blew** the **blue** kite **above** the trees.
3. **Do** you **know** where you will **live** when you **move**?

List 7

1. Will the wind **carry** my **pretty balloon off** to **Mississippi**?
2. Stan **added** a **letter** in the **middle** of the **spelling** word.
3. Is the artist **willing** to draw a **different pattern**?

List 8

1. The note he **received** told who is **getting** the prize.
2. Are you **coming** to the **swimming** party I'm **having**?
3. Connie **joked** about what **happened** after the party **ended**.

List 9

1. The **price** of **uniforms usually stayed** the same.
2. Her **niece tried** to **float** an ice **cube**.
3. Do you **mean** they **might show** us some tricks?

List 10

1. The **teacher** and her **children** went **everywhere together**.
2. Be **sure** to **finish** the **whole** job.
3. **Where** do you **think** we need to **search** for it?

List 11

1. **Everyone** came to school **without homework today**.
2. Let's play **basketball** or ride my **skateboard outside**.
3. Was **everybody** scared by the **earthquake**?

List 12

1. That **tough** kid **called** the **small** boy an **awful** name.
2. Bob **brought** his **strongest** rope **along** on our camping trip.
3. She **bought** a **drawing** of a cow sleeping on **straw**.

List 13

1. The **ladies cried** when the **story** was **finally** over.
2. My **family** gave me **toys** and **shoes** as a **surprise**.
3. The **shy lady studied** how to do magic tricks.

List 14

1. Is it **true** that the **school** has **good food**?
2. The **football** team is **due** to get new uniforms.
3. Maggie **chewed** on **cookies** until she was **full**.

List 15

1. He didn't **enjoy** using **poison** to **destroy** the rats.
2. The **boy joined** his dad for a **voyage** across the sea.
3. His **choice** was **oysters** and **chocolate** pudding for dinner.

List 16

1. **I'm** sure **we're** going where **they're** going.
2. Why **can't** they stay until six **o'clock**?
3. The clock **doesn't** work so **they're** always late.

List 17

1. You **should follow** that **group** to the old **house**.
2. My **cousin** ran **around town** until she **found** her dog.
3. **Would** you like to **own** a book **about** that **country**?

List 18

1. Did **April's** pet rabbit have **those tiny white babies**?
2. Pat **raised** the flag **over** her head.
3. We **used** the **menu** to choose dinner.

List 19

1. I'm too **tired** to **read** the book **again**.
2. Why do you **disagree** about the **other problem**?
3. **Does some of** the **money** need to be **given** to Mother?

List 20

1. The **giant's** golden **goose** was **gone**.
2. **Clean** up the spilled **cereal** and put it in the **carton**.
3. **Could** the **guards** save the **city** from **danger**?

List 21

1. Can I **learn** to be a **nurse** and **work** all around the **world**?
2. The **first word** the baby said was **bird**.
3. Burt **stirred** the **fire** and **turned** the meat on the grill.

List 22

1. Farmer Brown takes **care** of her **large horse** every **morning**.
2. **Aren't** you going to read the **warning** on the **chart**?
3. My **partner** had a **hard** trip to the **north** country.

List 23

1. The **thoughtless** boy was cold **because** he **threw** away his jacket.
2. It's **wonderful** to **watch water** fall over a cliff.
3. Who **taught** you how to **walk** when you were **one**?

List 24

1. Take two **dollars** to the **store** and buy some **sugar**.
2. **Doctor** Hunter said my leg will be **better** in **forty** days.
3. **Every** flower was a pretty **color** and had a sweet **odor**.

List 25

1. Her **nephew** was **unhappy** when he lost the **photograph**.
2. **Happily** his **cough** was better by **Friday**.
3. The **orphan** was **happier** after eating the **alphabet** soup.

List 26

1. My **neighbor** thinks she saw a **ghost climb** on a tree **limb**.
2. The postman **knew** the **wrong** name was **written** on the letter.
3. Cut the **knot** in the string and **unwrap** the gift.

List 27

1. A **fearless** man moved **slowly** and **quietly** past the lion.
2. If you work too **quickly** you will make **careless** mistakes.
3. Everyone is **joyful** when Tina tells her **funniest** jokes.

List 28

1. I **heard Mother** call a **friendly** greeting **early** this morning.
2. **Measure** some milk and **break** an egg into the bowl.
3. Sam's **brother** and his **friend** stayed there for **another year**.

List 29

1. A **knight** rode all **night** to deliver a **peace** offering to the king.
2. **Our** mother **wrote** her letter on a **piece** of pretty paper.
3. We must **wait** an **hour** for the bus to **their** house.

List 30

1. It's **all right** to open the **beautiful presents** now.
2. **People** went **straight** to the **hospital** after the train crash.
3. **Remember** to pack your **favorite clothes** for your **vacation**.

                       Building Spelling Skills 3-4 EMC 726

Name:

Spelling List

1

Read and spell	Copy and spell	Spell and check
1. said	_____	_____
2. ask	_____	_____
3. stand	_____	_____
4. catch	_____	_____
5. eight	_____	_____
6. afraid	_____	_____
7. away	_____	_____
8. always	_____	_____
9. playing	_____	_____
10. waved	_____	_____
11. takes	_____	_____
12. than	_____	_____
13. great	_____	_____
14. they	_____	_____
15. prey	_____	_____
16. _____ special word	_____	_____
17. _____ special word	_____	_____

fold

Name:

Visual Memory

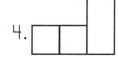

Fill in the boxes.

1.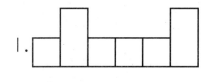

2.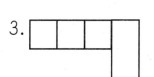

3.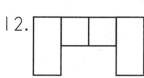

4.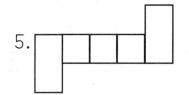

5.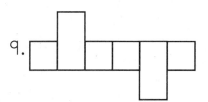

6.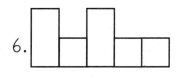

7.

8.

9.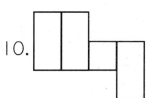

10.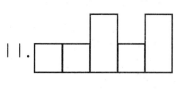

11.

12.

stand	waved	great	than	prey
afraid	they	playing	ask	takes
away	said	eight	catch	always

Edit Spelling

Cross out the misspelled words.

1. sed   said
2. eitgh   eight
3. great   grait
4. prey   drey
5. catsh   catch
6. afraid   ufraid
7. wavd   waved

8. they   thay
9. aks   ask
10. stend   stand
11. paling   playing
12. taks   takes
13. than   fhan
14. away   uway

25   Building Spelling Skills 3-4 EMC 726

Building Spelling Skills

Word Meaning

1

Fill in the missing word.

1. An octopus used its _____ tentacles to catch _____ to eat.

2. It _____ a long time to _____ my dog to give him a bath.

3. My little sister is _____ _____ of thunder and lightning.

4. _____ were _____ football at the park.

5. Marcus _____ his hand and _____ "Goodbye."

6. You must _____ far _____ from the campfire.

7. Will you _____ mother for a _____ big ice cream sundae?

takes	ask	always	catch	eight
afraid	away	stand	prey	waved
said	than	great	they	playing

Write sentences with _____ and _____ .

_____

_____

_____

_____

Building Spelling Skills

Name: _____

Phonics

Underline words with the long a sound (a in cake).
Put a circle around the letters that make the long a sound.

w<u>a</u>ve	catch	away	takes	great
ask	eight	stand	said	they
always	afraid	prey	than	playing

Structure

Add *ed* and *ing* to these words.

Add the endings.

1. play   _____   _____

2. ask   _____   _____

3. prey   _____   _____

4. paint   _____   _____

Drop *e* and add endings.

1. wave   _____   _____

2. smile   _____   _____

3. skate   _____   _____

4. bake   _____   _____

Name:

Spelling List 2

Read and spell	Copy and spell	Spell and check
1. next		
2. left		
3. help		
4. please		
5. believe		
6. many		
7. very		
8. been		
9. seen		
10. she		
11. between		
12. three		
13. easy		
14. sea		
15. leave		
16. _____ special word		
17. _____ special word		

fold

Building Spelling Skills

Name: _____

  2

Fill in the boxes.

1.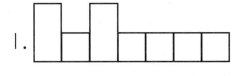

2.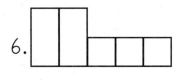

3.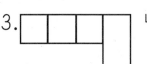

4.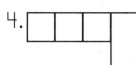

5.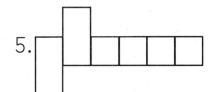

6.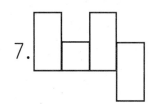

7. (boxes)

8.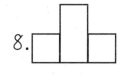

9.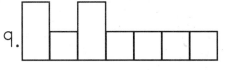

10.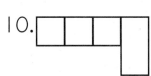

11.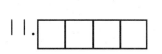

12.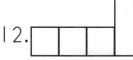

very	believe	next	easy	leave
been	please	help	between	she
seen	many	left	three	sea

 Edit Spelling

Mark the misspelled word.
Write it correctly on the line.

1. Plez help me fix my bike. _____

2. We have to leaf now. _____

3. It isn't eezy to ride a horse. _____

4. Have you ben to the park? _____

5. Park the car betwene the trees. _____

6. Did you belive his story? _____

7. I saw miny cows at his farm. _____

8. Jane had tree pet cats. _____

 Building Spelling Skills 3-4 EMC 726

Building Spelling Skills

Name:

Answer the questions.

1. What does **left** mean in this sentence?

   ## How many cookies are left?

   a. opposite of right
   b. remain
   c. were eaten

2. What is another word for ocean? _____

3. What is the opposite of …?

   a. difficult
   b. right
   c. he
   d. few
   e. stay

4. What word means "in the middle of two things"? _____

5. What word do you use if you want to show good manners? _____

6. Which word means you think something is true? _____

next	left	help	please	believe
many	very	been	seen	she
between	three	easy	sea	leave

Write sentences with _____ **and** _____ .

_____

_____

_____

_____

Building Spelling Skills

Name:

Word Study

2

Phonics

Underline words with the long e sound (e in me).
Put a circle around the letters that make the long e sound.

<u>thr(ee)</u>   left   she

please   believe   many

very   been   seen

help   between   leave

easy   sea   next

Structure

Write the spelling words that rhyme with these words.

1. merry _____   6. pea _____
2. any   _____   7. queen _____
3. sneeze _____   8. relieve _____
4. free _____   9. bee _____
5. yelp _____   10. lean _____

next	left	help	please	believe
many	very	been	seen	she
between	three	easy	sea	leave

©1998 by Evan-Moor Corp.   Building Spelling Skills 3-4 EMC 726

Building Spelling Skills

Name: _____

Spelling List 3

Read and spell	Copy and spell	Spell and check
1. pitch	_____	_____
2. drink	_____	_____
3. swim	_____	_____
4. life	_____	_____
5. while	_____	_____
6. I	_____	_____
7. my	_____	_____
8. light	_____	_____
9. buy	_____	_____
10. eye	_____	_____
11. which	_____	_____
12. find	_____	_____
13. why	_____	_____
14. kind	_____	_____
15. try	_____	_____
16._____ special word	_____	_____
17._____ special word	_____	_____

fold

Name:

Visual Memory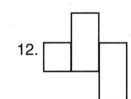

Fill in the boxes.

1.

2.

3.

4.

5.

6.

7.

8.

9.

10.

11.

12.

life	pitch	my	eye	why
drink	while	light	which	kind
try	I	buy	find	swim

Edit Spelling

Mark the misspelled words.
Write them correctly on the lines.

1. Mom needs to bie a lite for the lamp. _____ _____

2. Witch kind of drenk do you like best? _____ _____

3. Trie to catch the ball when I picth it. _____ _____

4. When I swem I get water in my aye. _____ _____

5. Eye like to by that kind of candy. _____ _____

Building Spelling Skills

Name:

Word Meaning

3

Fill in the blanks.

1. _____ have something in my _____ .
   eye   try   I

2. _____ did you _____ that kind of soft _____?
   buy   drink   why   try

3. _____ to the bottom of the pool and _____ to _____
   my lost ring.
   find   try   while   swim

4. _____ kind of _____ do you need?
   witch   while   which   light

5. Can you catch _____ I _____ the baseball?
   pitch   why   while   light

6. The words _____ and _____ rhyme.
   my   find   try   while

7. I have tried to be a _____ person all of my _____ .

Write sentences with _____ **and** _____ .

_____

_____

_____

_____

Building Spelling Skills

Name:

Word Study

3

Phonics

Underline words with the long i sound (i in kite).
Put a circle around the letters that make the long i sound.

life	drink	try
pitch	while	I
my	light	buy
eye	which	find
why	kind	swim

Word Families

Add letters to make new words.

ind	ile	ight	ink
_____ind	_____ile	_____ight	_____ink
_____ind	_____ile	_____ight	_____ink
_____ind	_____ile	_____ight	_____ink
_____ind	_____ile	_____ight	_____ink
_____ind	_____ile	_____ight	_____ink
_____ind	_____ile	_____ight	_____ink

35

Building Spelling Skills 3-4 EMC 726

Building Spelling Skills

Name:

Spelling List 4

Read and spell	Copy and spell	Spell and check
1. rocket		
2. pocket		
3. hold		
4. told		
5. often		
6. grow		
7. throne		
8. so		
9. sew		
10. most		
11. almost		
12. both		
13. coach		
14. open		
15. also		
16. _____ *special word*		
17. _____ *special word*		

fold

Name:

Visual Memory

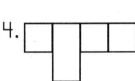

Fill in the boxes.

1.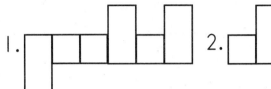
2.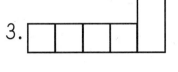
3.
4.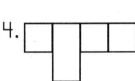

5.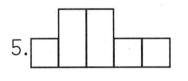
6.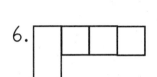
7.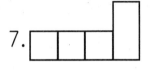
8.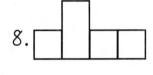

9.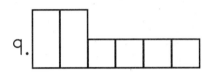
10.
11.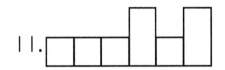
12.

rocket	hold	often	grow	so
pocket	told	also	sew	most
throne	almost	both	coach	open

Edit Spelling

Mark the misspelled word.

1. roket   rocket
2. whold   hold
3. often   offen
4. throne   thone
5. amolst   almost
6. bofh   both

7. coach   koach
8. allso   also
9. opun   open
10. grow   groe
11. tole   told
12. sowe   sew

Building Spelling Skills

Name: _____

Word Meaning

4

Answer the questions.

1. What could a king or queen sit on? _____

2. In what part of a jacket can you carry things? _____

3. Which two spelling words rhyme with **cold**? _____

4. What do you call a person that helps a team play better? _____

5. Which two spelling words sound the same but have different spellings? _____

6. What is the opposite of shut? _____

7. What transportation would an astronaut use? _____

8. What word goes in this sentence?

   Mother is going to _____ my Halloween costume.

rocket	hold	often	grow	so
pocket	told	also	sew	most
throne	almost	both	coach	open

Write sentences with _____ **and** _____ .

_____

_____

Name:

Word Study

Phonics

Underline words with the long o sound (o in go).
Put a circle around the letters that make the long o sound.

rocket	hold	throne
grow	so	pocket
told	also	sew
most	often	almost
both	coach	open

Structure

Write the words with one syllable.

1._____
2._____
3._____
4._____
5._____
6._____
7._____
8._____
9._____

Write the words with two syllables.

1._____
2._____
3._____
4._____
5._____
6._____

rocket	hold	often	both	almost
grow	so	pocket	coach	throne
told	also	sew	open	most

Name:

Spelling List

5

Read and spell	Copy and spell	Spell and check
1. under		
2. such		
3. much		
4. young		
5. touch		
6. use		
7. your		
8. you		
9. unit		
10. cute		
11. few		
12. new		
13. fuel		
14. human		
15. music		
16. _____ special word		
17. _____ special word		

fold

Building Spelling Skills

Name: _____

Visual Memory

Unscramble the letters.

1. chum _____

2. outch _____

3. sue _____

4. uoy _____

5. intu _____

6. wef _____

7. lufe _____

8. redun _____

9. chus _____

10. hunam _____

11. sicmu _____

12. gnuoy _____

under	such	much	young	touch
use	your	you	unit	fuel
few	new	cute	human	music

 ## Edit Spelling

Mark the misspelled word.
Write it correctly on the line.

1. Jim's dog ran undar the bed. _____

2. Do you like her noo coat? _____

3. What is yer name? _____

4. That's a kute baby. _____

5. Don't tuch the hot stove. _____

6. Ann's sister is a yung lady. _____

7. A fuo boys came to the party. _____

8. Do you like rap moosic? _____

   Building Spelling Skills 3-4 EMC 726

Name: _____

Word Meaning

5

Draw a picture to show what the sentence means.

Kate found her kitten hiding under the bed.	Dad pumped fuel into the tank of his new car.
The young boy played music.	A few pennies were in the cute piggy bank.
A human touched the tall tree.	How much is five times six?

       Building Spelling Skills 3-4 EMC 726

Name: _____

Word Study

5

Phonics

Underline words with the long u sound (u in use).
Put a circle around the letters that make the long u sound.

(u)se	such	few
young	music	under
your	you	unit
cute	much	new
fuel	human	touch

Rhyming Words

Write the spelling words that rhyme with these words.

1. crutch _____   6. flute _____
2. sung _____   7. few _____
3. thunder _____   8. jewel _____
4. shoes _____   9. Dutch _____
5. too _____   10. tour _____

Fill in the blanks with rhyming words.

1. Zeke hid _____ the bed when he heard _____.

2. They bought a _____ pairs of _____ shoes.

3. A _____ little girl played music on a _____.

     Building Spelling Skills 3-4 EMC 726

Name:

Spelling List

6

Read and spell	Copy and spell	Spell and check
1. save		
2. give		
3. have		
4. live		
5. move		
6. above		
7. alive		
8. alike		
9. to		
10. two		
11. too		
12. know		
13. do		
14. blew		
15. blue		
16. _____ special word		
17. _____ special word		

fold

Name:

Visual Memory

6

Fill in the missing letters.

____oo	____ike	____ew	____ow
____ue	____wo	____o	____o
____ove	____ove	____ave	____ave
____ive	____ive	____ive	

save	give	have	live	move
above	alike	alive	to	two
too	know	do	blew	blue

Edit Spelling

Mark the misspelled word.
Write it correctly on the line.

1. There were tow plants in the pot. _____

2. The girls looked ulike. _____

3. His new bike is blew. _____

4. Do you no what fish like to eat? _____

5. Can I hav a ride to school? _____

6. Will you geve me some milk? _____

7. Nat went too the zoo. _____

8. Moov your bike out of the street. _____

| Name: | # Word Meaning | 6 |

Fill in the missing words.

| to | two | too |

1. The little boy is _____ years old.

2. I want an ice cream cone _____.

3. Bring the plates _____ the table.

| blew | blue |

1. A strong wind _____ the leaves off the trees.

2. Did you see how _____ the sky was today?

| know | no |

1. When will you _____ if you can go on the trip?

2. There is _____ more peanut butter in the jar.

Write sentences with _____ **and** _____ .

_____

_____

_____

_____

Building Spelling Skills

Name: _____

Word Study

6

Phonics

Write each word in the correct box.

short vowel		long vowel		sound of o in to	
above	blue	give	live	move	too
blew	do	have	know	save	two

Past Tense

Write the past tense to these verbs.
Circle the irregular verb forms.

1. give _____   5. blow _____
2. move _____   6. do _____
3. live _____   7. have _____
4. know _____   8. save _____

Fill in the missing verb.

1. New people _____ in next door.
   (move)

2. Do you _____ how to make toast?
   (know)

3. The man _____ up balloons and made animals out of them.
   (blow)

4. Have you _____ the money you need for a new bike?
   (save)

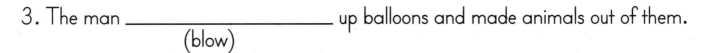

Name:

Spelling List

7

Read and spell	Copy and spell	Spell and check
1. missed		
2. willing		
3. balloon		
4. spelling		
5. pretty		
6. still		
7. off		
8. added		
9. letter		
10. different		
11. pattern		
12. middle		
13. Mississippi		
14. zipper		
15. carry		
16. _____ special word		
17. _____ special word		

fold

Name:

Visual Memory

Find the words hiding in this puzzle.

```
m  b  a  l  l  o  o  n  o  f  f  x  l
i  i  l  l  z  i  p  m  i  d  d  l  e
s  o  s  w  i  l  l  i  n  g  i  z  t
s  c  a  s  s  y  z  g  o  o  f  a  t
e  t  s  t  i  l  l  i  u  v  f  d  e
d  g  i  p  a  s  l  i  p  p  e  d  r
c  o  l  r  o  w  s  n  o  p  r  e  p
a  z  l  e  t  t  r  i  n  e  e  d  r
r  p  a  t  t  e  r  n  p  l  n  r  e
r  o  p  t  d  i  f  f  u  p  t  z  t
y  f  e  y  o  s  p  e  l  l  i  n  g
```

added
balloon
carry
different
letter
middle
missed
Mississippi
off
pattern
pretty
spelling
still
willing
zipper

Edit Spelling

Circle the correct spelling.

1. misst   missed   mised
2. baloon   balloon   ballon
3. pretty   pertty   preddy
4. ledder   eter   letter
5. differunt   different   diferent
6. patturn   patern   pattern
7. carry   cerry   karry
8. ovv   off   uff
9. ziper   zipper   zippir

Building Spelling Skills

Name:

Word Meaning

7

Fill in the missing words.

1. Did you study for the _____ test?

2. We sailed on the _____ River.

3. I bought a shiny red _____ for my little sister.

4. The _____ on her jacket broke.

5. Will you help me _____ this box into the house?

6. Who wrote you that _____?

7. I went to a _____ school last year.

8. Mother cut out the _____ for a new dress she is making.

added	balloon	carry	different	pattern
middle	missed	off	Mississippi	letter
pretty	spelling	still	willing	zipper

Write sentences with _____ **and** _____ .

_____

_____

_____

_____

Building Spelling Skills

Name: _____

Word Study

⭐⭐ 7

Phonics

Answer these questions.

1. What sound is made by the suffix **ed** in these words?

   missed _____ added _____ spelled _____

2. Which of the spelling words fit this rule?

   In most words with two or more syllables the final **y** has the sound of long **e**.

   _____   _____

3. What changes would you make to these words when adding the suffix **ed**?

   spell_____

   carry_____

Structure

Divide the words into syllables and write them.

> Divide:
> • between a base word and ending - **sell ing**
> • between double consonants - **kit ten**

1. missing _____
2. balloon _____
3. spelling _____
4. pretty _____
5. added _____
6. letter _____
7. middle _____
8. willing _____
9. zipper _____
10. carry _____
11. pattern _____
12. different _____

Name:

Spelling List

8

Read and spell	Copy and spell	Spell and check
1. swimming		
2. swam		
3. getting		
4. coming		
5. came		
6. having		
7. doing		
8. ended		
9. happened		
10. happening		
11. started		
12. joked		
13. received		
14. smiled		
15. smiling		
16. _____ special word		
17. _____ special word		

fold

Building Spelling Skills

Name: _____

Visual Memory

Circle the missing letters.
Write them on the lines.

1. swi____ing   **m or mm**
2. ca____e   **m or mm**
3. ge____ing   **t or tt**
4. star____ed   **t or tt**
5. en____ed   **d or dd**
6. ha____ened   **p or pp**

7. smi____ed   **l or ll**
8. sti____   **l or ll**
9. swa____   **m or mm**
10. co____ing   **m or mm**
11. jo____ed   **k or kk**
12. recei____ed   **v or vv**

 Edit Spelling

Write the correct spelling of these words.

1. swiming _____
2. geting _____
3. comeng _____
4. haveng _____
5. dooing _____

6. happend _____
7. happining _____
8. joket _____
9. smild _____
10. kame _____

Fill in the missing word using the correct ending.

1. Raul _____ piano lessons this week.
   (start)
2. Have you _____ your birthday present yet?
   (receive)
3. Why is she _____?
   (smile)

Building Spelling Skills

Name:	**Word Meaning**	 8

Fill in the missing words.

swam   swimming

1. We _____ in the river yesterday.
   They are going _____ today.

---

happened   happening

2. What is _____ in that television program?
   That is the same thing that _____ on the last show.

---

came   coming

3. Who is _____ to the band concert?
   Many people _____ to hear us play last year.

---

smiling   smiled

4. Karen _____ when she opened the front door.
   Why was she _____?

Write sentences with _____ and _____ .

_____

_____

_____

_____

Name:

Word Study

8

Verb Tense

Write the past tense of these words.
Circle the irregular verbs.

1. joke _____
2. swim _____
3. happen _____
4. end _____
5. come _____
6. do _____

7. smile _____
8. have _____
9. receive _____
10. hide _____
11. call _____
12. fly _____

Structure

Add the suffix *ing* to the word.
Mark what you did to change the word.

	no change	double final consonant	drop e, add ing
1. swim ming		✓	
2. get_____			
3. receive_____			
4. come_____			
5. have_____			
6. do_____			
7. smile_____			
8. end_____			
9. happen_____			
10. start_____			
11. joke_____			

 Building Spelling Skills 3-4 EMC 726

Name: _____

Spelling List 9

Read and spell	Copy and spell	Spell and check
1. way	_____	_____
2. these	_____	_____
3. niece	_____	_____
4. might	_____	_____
5. show	_____	_____
6. float	_____	_____
7. brain	_____	_____
8. mean	_____	_____
9. close	_____	_____
10. tried	_____	_____
11. cube	_____	_____
12. uniform	_____	_____
13. stayed	_____	_____
14. price	_____	_____
15. usually	_____	_____
16. _____ special word	_____	_____
17. _____ special word	_____	_____

fold

Building Spelling Skills 3-4 EMC 726

Building Spelling Skills

Name: _____

Visual Memory

Unscramble and match the correct spelling.

yaw	close	beuc	price
thees	niece	ripce	float
neice	way	mitgh	cube
hows	these	foalt	uniform
anme	tried	niarb	brain
locse	mean	formuni	stayed
deirt	show	edstay	might

Edit Spelling

Mark the misspelled word.
Spell it correctly on the line.

1. My new band youniform is silver. _____

2. Cloze the door when you go out. _____

3. The boys mite go fishing next Saturday. _____

4. Put an ice kube in that glass. _____

5. Grandpa staid in bed until 8 o'clock. _____

6. The fox tryed to catch a rabbit. _____

7. Can you shoo me how to play this game? _____

8. Did you ever drink a rootbeer flote? _____

©1998 by Evan-Moor Corp.   57   Building Spelling Skills 3-4 EMC 726

Name:

Word Meaning

Complete the crossword puzzle.

Across
1. not kind
4. the cost
5. special clothing
8. shut
9. this one and this one

Down
2. a girl relative
3. what you think with
6. opposite of sink
7. a six-sided square
10. remain

brain	niece
close	price
cube	stay
float	these
mean	uniform

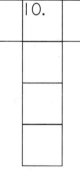

Building Spelling Skills

Name: _____

Word Study

Phonics

Write the long vowel sound you hear.

1. way _____
2. these _____
3. niece _____
4. show _____
5. float _____
6. brain _____
7. mean _____

8. close _____
9. tried _____
10. cube _____
11. uniform _____
12. stayed _____
13. price _____

Bonus: usually _____ _____ _____

Structure

Add *ed* to the words.

no change - play<u>ed</u>	change *y* to *i* and add *ed*
1. stay _____	_____
2. try _____	_____
3. float _____	_____
4. show _____	_____
5. cry _____	_____
6. hurry _____	_____
7. plant _____	_____
8. worry _____	_____

Fill in the missing word.

1. The cook _____ a huge cake for the wedding.
   (bake)

2. A little mouse _____ across the kitchen floor.
   (scurry)

3. The hungry mole _____ under the ground looking for worms to eat.
   (burrow)

Building Spelling Skills 3-4 EMC 726

Building Spelling Skills

Name:

Read and spell	Copy and spell	Spell and check
1. children	_____	_____
2. search	_____	_____
3. teacher	_____	_____
4. reached	_____	_____
5. think	_____	_____
6. together	_____	_____
7. with	_____	_____
8. where	_____	_____
9. everywhere	_____	_____
10. short	_____	_____
11. push	_____	_____
12. finish	_____	_____
13. sure	_____	_____
14. who	_____	_____
15. whole	_____	_____
16. _____ special word	_____	_____
17. _____ special word	_____	_____

fold

Name:

Visual Memory

10

Fill in the missing letters.

ch	wh	th	sh

1. sear_____

2. fini_____

3. _____ink

4. _____ort

5. ole _____

6. wi_____

7. _____ere

8. _____ildren

9. toge_____er

10. tea_____er

11. every_____ere

12. rea_____ed

Edit Spelling

Mark the misspelled words.
Write them correctly on the lines.

1. Hoo ate htat hole cake?

_____   _____   _____

2. Can the childrun poosh the wagon?

_____   _____

3. We can go when you finnish the shirt story.

_____   _____

4. Where do you tink we should serch for it?

_____   _____

5. Will you and your teecher go there togepher?

_____   _____

Building Spelling Skills

Word Meaning

Answer the questions.

1. Write the names for people.

   _____   _____

2. What word means "all places"? _____

3. What do you do when you use your brain? _____

4. What word means "to complete something"? _____

5. What word means "to look for something that is lost"? _____

6. What is the opposite of...?

   part   _____

   long   _____

   apart   _____

7. Circle the words that rhyme.

        new   who   why   shoe

8. Circle the words that begin with the same sound as she.

        show   seal   sure

children	search	teacher	reached	think
together	with	where	short	push
everywhere	finish	sure	who	whole

Write sentences with _____ **and** _____ .

_____

_____

_____

Building Spelling Skills

Name: _____

Word Study

10

Phonics

| ch | th | wh | sh |

Fill in the missing letters to make words on the spelling list.

1. _____ildren
2. sear_____
3. _____ink
4. _____ole
5. _____ere
6. fini_____

7. toge_____er
8. pu_____
9. tea_____er
10. wi_____
11. _____ort
12. _____o

Structure

Circle the number of syllables you hear.

1. together   1 2 3 4
2. who   1 2 3 4
3. search   1 2 3 4
4. teacher   1 2 3 4
5. reached   1 2 3 4
6. think   1 2 3 4
7. with   1 2 3 4
8. everywhere   1 2 3 4

9. sure   1 2 3 4
10. children   1 2 3 4
11. whole   1 2 3 4
12. finish   1 2 3 4
13. push   1 2 3 4
14. where   1 2 3 4
15. short   1 2 3 4

Name:

Spelling List

11

Read and spell	Copy and spell	Spell and check
1. into		
2. today		
3. without		
4. something		
5. become		
6. upon		
7. myself		
8. everybody		
9. everyone		
10. maybe		
11. outside		
12. basketball		
13. homework		
14. skateboard		
15. earthquake		
16. _____		
special word		
17. _____		
special word		

fold

Building Spelling Skills

Name: _____

Find the words hiding in this puzzle.

e	v	e	r	y	b	o	d	y	e	s	s
v	a	n	h	o	m	e	w	o	r	k	o
e	r	r	t	o	d	a	y	m	a	a	m
r	w	i	t	h	o	u	t	y	b	t	e
y	o	u	i	h	e	r	o	s	e	e	t
o	u	t	n	o	q	u	d	e	c	b	h
n	e	w	t	t	u	u	y	l	o	o	i
e	u	p	o	n	t	o	a	f	m	a	n
m	a	y	b	e	m	y	s	k	e	r	g
o	u	t	o	u	t	s	i	d	e	d	o
b	a	s	k	e	t	b	a	l	l	i	n

become
basketball
earthquake
everybody
everyone
homework
into
maybe
myself
outside
skateboard
something
today
upon
without

Edit Spelling

Mark the misspelled words.
Write them correctly on the lines.

Yesterday I finished my homewerk by misef. Then I went owtside and rode
my skatbord to the park. Everbody was playing baskutball.

Evrywon was having fun when sumthing happened. The ground started to
shake. It was an erthquak! When it stopped, we ran home wifout the basketball.
Maybee it is still at the park.

1. _____
2. _____
3. _____
4. _____
5. _____
6. _____
7. _____
8. _____
9. _____
10. _____
11. _____

Building Spelling Skills

Name: _____

Word Meaning

Fill in the missing words.

1. Maurice received a _____ and a _____ for his birthday.

2. An _____ made cracks in the _____ walls of our house.

3. Our teacher said, " There is no _____ _____

4. _____ strange ran _____ the barn.

5. Once _____ a time there was a dragon that couldn't fly.

6. Do you want to _____ a professional soccer player someday

7. Can you wash the car _____ any help?

8. _____ is gone so I am all by _____.

become	basketball	earthquake	into	everyone
homework	skateboard	maybe	myself	outside
something	upon	today	everybody	without

Write sentences with _____ **and** _____ .

_____

_____

_____

_____

Building Spelling Skills

Name: _____

Word Study

Phonics

Mark the vowels in these words.
Put an x above the silent e.

| long – āpe̷ˣ | short – hăt | schwa – ə̇f | other sounds – (out) |

1. into
2. today
3. without
4. something
5. become

6. upon
7. maybe
8. outside
9. basketball
10. homework

Compound Words

Complete the compound words from your spelling list.

1. basket_____
2. be_____
3. earth_____
4. every_____
5. _____one
6. _____work
7. in_____
8. _____self

9. _____be
10. out_____
11. skate_____
12. some_____
13. to_____
14. _____on
15. _____out

with	up	day	thing	board
quake	ball	to	every	body
come	home	my	may	side

Name:

Spelling List

12

Read and spell	Copy and spell	Spell and check
1. awful		
2. called		
3. falling		
4. mall		
5. small		
6. straw		
7. drawing		
8. strongest		
9. longer		
10. song		
11. along		
12. bought		
13. brought		
14. rough		
15. tough		
16. _____ special word		
17. _____ special word		

fold

Building Spelling Skills

Name: _____

Visual Memory

12

Unscramble the word.
Write it on the line.

1. awflu _____
2. decall _____
3. llam _____
4. gons _____
5. malls _____
6. olang _____
7. rouhg _____
8. lnoger _____
9. traws _____
10. darwing _____
11. srongtest _____
12. flaling _____

falling	awful	called	mall	straw
small	drawing	strongest	longer	tough
song	along	bought	brought	rough

Edit Spelling

Mark the mistakes.
Write the correct spellings on the lines.

1. Adam made an ahful mistake.

   _____

2. Put the smal starw in the cold drink.

   _____   _____

3. He made a drawn of the stronust man in the world.

   _____   _____

4. Anna bawght it at the moll.

   _____   _____

5. Will you sing a longar sogn next time?

   _____   _____

 Building Spelling Skills 3-4 EMC 726

Name:	**Word Meaning**	12

Answer the questions.

1. Which word means "terrible"?_____

2. What could be used to make a bed for a farm animal? _____

3. What do you call a place with many shops all together?_____

4. Which word is a kind of picture?_____

5. Circle the words that rhyme.   tough   stuff   bought   rough

6. What is the opposite of...?
   sold _____   shorter _____
   large _____   weakest _____
   smooth _____

7. What does straw mean in this sentence?

   I used a plastic <u>straw</u> to drink my soda.

   a. dried hay
   b. thin, hollow tube
   c. material for making brooms

falling	awful	called	mall	straw
small	drawing	strongest	longer	tough
song	along	bought	brought	rough

Write sentences with _____ **and** _____ .

_____

_____

_____

_____

Name:

Word Study

12

Phonics

Underline words with the sound of *a* in all. Circle the letters that make the sound.

(aw)ful	called	tough
mall	song	along
rough	bought	straw
strongest	falling	brought
small	drawing	longer

Structure

Add *er* or *est* to make a comparison.

	faster	fastest
1. strong	_____	_____
2. long	_____	_____
3. small	_____	_____
4. rough	_____	_____
5. tough	_____	_____

1. That wrestler is the _____ man I've ever seen.
   (strong)

2. Is a rabbit _____ than a cat?
   (small)

3. Mrs. Martin had the _____ bath towels I've ever felt.
   (rough)

4. Billy is the _____ kid on our block.
   (tough)

5. The yellow bus is _____ than our truck.
   (long)

Name:

Spelling List

13

Read and spell	Copy and spell	Spell and check
1. lady		
2. ladies		
3. surprise		
4. surprises		
5. toys		
6. shoes		
7. shy		
8. cry		
9. cried		
10. study		
11. studied		
12. story		
13. only		
14. finally		
15. family		
16. _____		
special word		
17. _____		
special word		

fold

Name: _____

Visual Memory

13

Fill in the missing syllable to make spelling words.

1. la_____

2. _____ily

3. on_____

4. _____prises

5. _____dies

6. stu_____

7. fi_____ly

8. _____ry

9. _____ied

10. sur_____

Edit Spelling

Mark the misspelled words.
Write them correctly on the lines.

1. The children gave Mother a big suprise. _____

2. Put on your shoos before you go outside. _____

3. The baby cryed for his bottle. _____

4. Do you have a big famuly? _____

5. Two ladys sang a song. _____

6. Did you enjoy the storie? _____

7. The game was finelly over. _____

8. Have you studied for the math test? _____

| Name: | # Word Meaning | 13 |

Fill in the missing words.

1. What _____ was in that large box?
   surprise   surprises

2. Both _____ bought new hats.
   lady   ladies

3. Did he _____ clean his bedroom?
   finally   family

4. She wants to _____ the violin.
   study   studied

5. The new girl was _____ on her first day at school.
   cry   shy

6. How many people are in your _____?
   finally   family

7. My grandfather is full of funny _____ that make me laugh.
   surprise   surprises

8. I was very sad when my best friend moved away.
   I _____ for a long time.
   cry   cried

Write sentences with _____ **and** _____ .

_____

_____

_____

_____

Building Spelling Skills

Name: _____

Phonics — Write words in the correct boxes.

y says i	y says e
1. _____	1. _____
2. _____	2. _____
3. _____	3. _____
4. _____	4. _____
5. _____	5. _____
6. _____	6. _____

cry	only	story	my
lady	shy	family	funny
study	why	fly	try

Plural Forms — Write the plural form of these words. Mark what you did to change the word.

	add s	drop e, add es	change y to i and add es
1. lady _____ladies_____			✓
2. toy _____			
3. story _____			
4. shoe _____			
5. family _____			
6. rocket _____			
7. niece _____			

Fill in the missing word.

1. Both _____ had on a red dress.
   (lady)

2. Will you read me a _____ before I go to bed?
   (story)

3. Mother's two _____ are coming to stay with us.
   (niece)

Building Spelling Skills

Name:

Read and spell	Copy and spell	Spell and check
1. looked		
2. good		
3. brook		
4. football		
5. cookie		
6. stood		
7. full		
8. put		
9. food		
10. school		
11. truth		
12. room		
13. true		
14. chew		
15. due		
16. _____ special word		
17. _____ special word		

fold

Building Spelling Skills

Name:

Visual Memory

14

Find the words hiding in the puzzle.

```
f  g  t  r  u  t  h  c  h  f
l  o  o  k  e  d  r  o  c  u
f  o  o  d  o  o  k  o  o  l
t  d  p  t  c  h  e  w  o  l
r  u  u  u  b  r  o  o  k  m
u  e  s  p  t  a  t  h  i  h
e  s  c  h  o  o  l  x  e  e
n  o  s  t  o  o  d  l  m  w
```

brook
chew
cookie
due
food
football
full
good
looked
put
room
school
stood
true
truth

Edit Spelling

Cross out the misspelled words.
Spell them correctly on the lines.

luked   fud   truth

good   full   deu

brook   poot   chew

futbal   stood   troo

cookee   schol   ruum

_____   _____   _____

_____   _____   _____

_____   _____   _____

© 1998 by Evan-Moor Corp.

Building Spelling Skills 3-4 EMC 726

Name:

Word Meaning

14

Complete the crossword puzzle.

Across
1. something to eat
3. type of sports equipment
7. a small stream
9. to crush with your teeth
10. opposite of bad

Down
1. opposite of empty
2. a sweet treat
4. that which is true
5. used your eyes to see
6. not a lie
8. where you go to learn

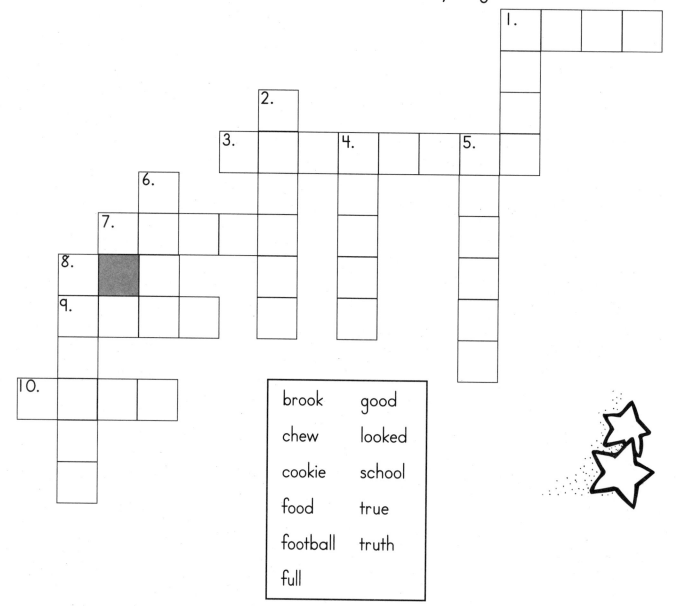

brook   good

chew   looked

cookie   school

food   true

football   truth

full

Building Spelling Skills

Name: _____

Word Study

14

Phonics

Write the words in the correct boxes.

sound of *u* in push	sound of *o* in do
1. _____	1. _____
2. _____	2. _____
3. _____	3. _____
4. _____	4. _____
5. _____	5. _____
6. _____	6. _____
7. _____	7. _____
8. _____	

looked	good	truth	put	stood
food	brook	room	true	full
school	football	cookie	chew	due

Antonyms

Write the opposite words.

1. empty _____
2. awful _____
3. sat _____

4. remove _____
5. lie _____
6. false _____

true	put
good	stood
chew	full
due	truth

Fill in the missing word.

1. Put the _____ milk carton in the refrigerator.

2. Can you _____ this book on the top shelf?

3. The band members _____ in lines waiting for the parade to begin.

©1998 by Evan-Moor Corp.

Building Spelling Skills 3-4 EMC 726

Name:

Spelling List 15

Read and spell	Copy and spell	Spell and check
1. pointing		
2. oily		
3. boy		
4. voice		
5. oyster		
6. voyage		
7. loyal		
8. joined		
9. coin		
10. choice		
11. poison		
12. destroy		
13. enjoy		
14. choose		
15. chocolate		
16. _____ special word		
17. _____ special word		

fold

Building Spelling Skills

Name:

Unscramble the words.
Match to the correct spelling.

yoil	voice	ocin	coin
cevoi	oily	ingpoint	joined
soyter	boy	cocholate	choice
joyen	voyage	edjoin	chocolate
yob	oyster	oichce	pointing
agevoy	loyal	sonpoi	destroy
loyla	enjoy	troydes	poison

 Edit Spelling

Mark the misspelled words.
Write them correctly on the lines.

1. My choyse is chocklate.

   _____   _____

2. Did you injoy your voyege?

   _____   _____

3. He will distroy the weeds with poisen.

   _____   _____

4. The little doy is pointing at an oister.

   _____   _____

5. Which coyn did he chose?

   _____   _____

     Building Spelling Skills 3-4 EMC 726

Building Spelling Skills

Name:

Word Meaning

15

Fill in the missing words.

1. We ate _____ on our sea _____.

  poison   coins   oysters   voyage

2. _____ cake is always Paul's _____.

  Oyster   Chocolate   choose   choice

3. Did that _____ _____ his toy truck?

  joined   boy   destroy   loyal

4. Why are you _____ at that gold _____?

  joined   coin   pointing   oily

5. Don't use a loud _____ while the baby is taking a nap.

  enjoy   choice   voice   coin

6. Lock the box of insect _____ in a cupboard.

  chocolate   poison   oyster   choice

7. I always _____ stories about kings and

  their _____ knights.

  loyal   voyage   destroy   enjoy

Write sentences with _____ **and** _____ .

_____

_____

_____

_____

Building Spelling Skills

Name: _____

Word Study

15

Phonics

oi   oy

Fill in the missing sounds.

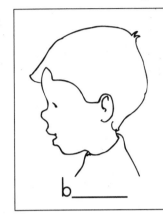 b_____

 _____ster

 p_____son

 c_____n

1. _____ly
2. ch_____ce
3. v_____ce
4. l_____al
5. p_____nting
6. destr_____
7. enj_____
8. j_____ned

Structure

Add endings to change the verbs.

	s or **es**	**ed**	**ing**
1. point	_____	_____	_____
2. join	_____	_____	_____
3. smile	_____	_____	_____
4. finish	_____	_____	_____

Add endings to the verbs to complete the sentences.

1. Norman was _____ at the funny television show.
   (smile)

2. The short hand on a clock _____ to the hour.
   (point)

3. Betty always _____ her work before she plays.
   (finish)

4. Carlos is _____ the Boy Scouts.
   (join)

Name:

Spelling List

16

Read and spell	Copy and spell	Spell and check
1. don't		
2. didn't		
3. I'll		
4. I'm		
5. it's		
6. let's		
7. they're		
8. we're		
9. doesn't		
10. o'clock		
11. won't		
12. wouldn't		
13. its		
14. can't		
15. that's		
16. _____ special word		
17. _____ special word		

fold

Building Spelling Skills

Name:

Put the apostrophe in the correct place.

1. dont
2. didnt
3. Ill
4. thats
5. its
6. cant

7. lets
8. theyre
9. were
10. doesnt
11. oclock
12. wont

 Edit Spelling

Mark the misspelled words.
Write them correctly on the lines.

1. They ~~dint~~ like the scary movie.    didn't

2. Did you know were moving when school is out?   _____

3. Why duzn't the clock work?   _____

4. Their going to Disneyland next week.   _____

5. Tat's Cindy's pet hamster.   _____

6. Its too hot to play outside today.   _____

7. Let's ask why they kan't come over.   _____

8. A'll bring my football to the game.   _____

         Building Spelling Skills 3-4 EMC 726

Name:

Word Meaning

16

Write the contractions to complete the crossword puzzle.
Don't forget to include the apostrophe.

Across

3. of the clock
6. does not
7. will not
8. would not
10. they are
11. it is

Down

1. do not
2. I will
4. cannot
5. let us
6. did not
8. we are
9. that is

Building Spelling Skills 3-4 EMC 726

Building Spelling Skills

Name: _____

Word Study

 16

Phonics

Answer the questions.

1. What is the long form of these words?

> won't_____
>
> don't_____

2. Which spelling means "belonging to it"?

> its   it's

3. Which words can these contractions stand for?

> 's – as is us
>
> n't – can next not
>
> 're – were are am

4. Which spelling means "I will"?

> Ill   I'll

Structure

What letters are removed to make the contraction?

long form	contraction	missing letters
1. do not	don't	o
2. we are	_____	_____
3. they are	_____	_____
4. it is	_____	_____
5. would not	_____	_____
6. cannot	_____	_____
7. I am	_____	_____
8. that is	_____	_____
9. does not	_____	_____
10. did not	_____	_____
11. I will	_____	_____
12. let us		

Building Spelling Skills 3-4 EMC 726

Name:

Spelling List

17

Read and spell	Copy and spell	Spell and check
1. follow		
2. below		
3. own		
4. grown		
5. town		
6. ground		
7. around		
8. found		
9. about		
10. house		
11. group		
12. would		
13. should		
14. country		
15. cousin		
16. _____ special word		
17. _____ special word		

fold

Name: _____

Visual Memory

17

Fill in the missing letters.

ou	ow

1. t____n

2. h____se

3. gr____p

4. f____nd

5. foll____

6. c____sin

7. ab____t

8. ____n

9. bel____

10. w____ld

11. ar____nd

12. gr____n

13. c____ntry

14. sh____ld

15. gr____nd

Edit Spelling

Mark the misspelled words in the paragraph.
Write the correct spelling on the lines.

My kussin went with a grup of children from toun on a hike. They fallowed a path bello a small hill. They walked arownd a grove of trees and saw a herd of cows resting on the groun. Soon it was time to go to my cuzin's howse for lunch.

_____   _____   _____

_____   _____   _____

Building Spelling Skills

Name: _____

Word Meaning

17

Fill in the missing words.

1. The prairie dog _____ is under the _____ .

   | below town country ground |

2. My _____ lives in a _____ across the ocean.

   | group country cousin around |

3. A large _____ of visitors stayed at our _____ .

   | house cousin group own |

4. The farmer's corn crop _____ be _____ by now.

   | would own grown should |

5. _____ you _____ me up the ladder?

   | Would Should below follow |

6. Pirate Pete _____ the treasure _____ the ground.

   | found would below follow |

7. Kelly looked all _____ trying to find her lost shoe.

   | around below ground house |

8. Do you have your _____ computer at home?

   | grown town own below |

Write sentences with _____ **and** _____ .

_____

_____

_____

Building Spelling Skills

Name: _____

Word Study

17

Phonics

Write words in the correct boxes.

sound of o in go	sound of ow in cow	sound of oo in too	sound of u in up	sound of u in put
	grown	follow	around	below
	town	country	about	should
	found	would	own	could
	group	soup	cousin	

Rhyming Words

Write the words that rhyme.

1. brown _____

2. shout _____

3. mouse _____

4. dozen _____

5. soup _____

6. could _____ _____

7. show _____ _____

8. ground _____ _____

9. bone _____

own
grown
below
about
house
group
town
ground
around
cousin
follow
would
should
country
found

Building Spelling Skills 3-4 EMC 726

Name:

Spelling List

18

Read and spell	Copy and spell	Spell and check
1. April		
2. babies		
3. over		
4. hello		
5. even		
6. we		
7. silent		
8. tiny		
9. menu		
10. future		
11. dear		
12. raise		
13. white		
14. used		
15. those		
16. _____ special word		
17. _____ special word		

fold

Name:

Visual Memory

18

Match the parts to make words.
Write the words on the lines.

1. A   ver
2. e   pril
3. ba   ny
4. si   u
5. o   bies
6. hell   ven
7. ti   lent
8. men   ture
9. fu   o

1. _____
2. _____
3. _____
4. _____
5. _____
6. _____
7. _____
8. _____
9. _____

Edit Spelling

Mark the misspelled words.
Write the words correctly on the lines.

1. My grandmother says all babys are deer.

   _____ _____

2. Mr. Martin is going to raize tiney roses in his garden.

   _____ _____

3. It was sylent in the cave until someone yelled heloo.

   _____ _____

4. Last Aprul we painted our fence whyte.

   _____ _____

5. The teacher yousd thoze books with her class.

   _____ _____

Building Spelling Skills

Name:	**Word Meaning** 

Answer the questions.

1. What do you use to choose a meal at a restaurant? _____

2. Which word means...?

   time that hasn't happened yet   _____

   above something   _____

   not new   _____

   a greeting   _____

   no sound   _____

3. Which three words could describe young rabbits?

   _____ _____ _____

4. How do you change the word baby to make it mean more than one baby?

   _____

5. What month comes after March? _____

April	babies	over	hello	even
we	silent	tiny	menu	future
dear	raise	white	used	those

Write sentences with _____ **and** _____ .

_____

_____

_____

_____

| Name: | **Word Study** |  18 |

Phonics

Write the words in the correct boxes.

Long a	Long o	Long e	Long i	Long u
	April raised	used	over	
	menu dear	those	even silent	
	we white	future	hello	

Structure

Divide these words into syllables.
Circle the open syllable in each word.

| open | ⓞ pen |

1. April _____ _____

2. babies _____ _____

3. over _____ _____

4. hello _____ _____

5. even _____ _____

6. lady _____ _____

7. silent _____ _____

8. tiny _____ _____

9. menu _____ _____

10. future _____ _____

Bonus: vacation _____ _____

Name:

Spelling List

19

Read and spell	Copy and spell	Spell and check
1. disagree		
2. again		
3. given		
4. other		
5. money		
6. problem		
7. does		
8. of		
9. some		
10. laid		
11. change		
12. tired		
13. read		
14. nice		
15. lower		
16. _____ *special word*		
17. _____ *special word*		

fold

Building Spelling Skills

Name: _____

Find the spelling words hiding in this puzzle.

```
a  g  a  i  n  c  h  a  n  g  e  p
l  a  i  d  p  r  o  n  i  o  x  r
o  o  s  v  o  u  t  t  c  c  f  o
w  m  o  n  e  y  h  r  e  a  d  b
e  e  m  g  q  n  e  b  y  n  o  l
r  h  e  e  t  i  r  e  d  t  e  e
a  g  d  i  s  a  g  r  e  e  s  m
```

again
change
disagree
does
given
laid
lower
money
nice
of
other
problem
read
some
tired

 Edit Spelling

Mark the misspelled words.
Write the correct spelling on the lines.

Jack had a prblum yesterday. He wanted to red a good book
so he went to a nyce book store. Jack picke out a book and handed
his muney to the clerk.

Jack said to the clerk, "This is not the write chanje."

The clerk counted the monny agin. Jack was rite. The clerk
gave him some more mony and Jack went home to reed his book.

_____   _____   _____

_____   _____   _____

_____   _____   _____

_____   _____   _____

Building Spelling Skills

Name:

Word Meaning

19

Fill in the missing word.

1. _____ Arthur have enough _____ to buy a ticket?

2. Did the _____ lady help you solve your _____?

3. I _____ with what I just _____ in the newspaper.

4. Margo was too _____ after the game to _____ her clothes before she went to town.

5. My hen _____ some _____ her eggs in the weeds behind the chicken coop.

6. Let's _____ the sailboat into the lake _____.

7. Harry was _____ five dollars for cutting Mrs. Murphy's lawn.

8. Would you like to have _____ of my chocolate bar?

again	change	disagree	does	given
laid	lower	money	nice	of
other	problem	read	some	tired

Write sentences with _____ **and** _____ .

_____

_____

_____

_____

Building Spelling Skills 3-4 EMC 726

Building Spelling Skills

Name:

Phonics

Underline the words that have the schwa sound.
Circle the letters that make the sound.

a̲bout	same	h̲o̲ney

1. disagree
2. again
3. lower
4. does
5. change

6. tired
7. given
8. nice
9. read
10. other

11. problem
12. some
13. money
14. of

Structure

Add the prefix *dis* to these words.
Match the new words to their meaning.

1. _____honest
2. _____armed
3. _____continued
4. _____agreement
5. _____like
6. _____courage
7. _____ability

a. have a feeling against something
b. difference of opinion
c. having no weapons
d. not truthful
e. loss or lack of powers
f. put an end to; stopped
g. take away someone's hopes

Fill in the missing word.

1. The police _____ the robber.
2. She had a _____ with her best friend.
3. The store _____ products that did not sell.
4. I _____ liver and onions.
5. The man's _____ keeps him in a wheelchair.

Name:

Spelling List

20

Read and spell	Copy and spell	Spell and check
1. city		
2. cereal		
3. face		
4. could		
5. guess		
6. huge		
7. age		
8. danger		
9. goose		
10. gone		
11. coast		
12. clean		
13. guard		
14. giant		
15. carton		
16. _____ special word		
17. _____ special word		

fold

Building Spelling Skills

Name: _____

Find the words hiding in this puzzle.

```
c  e  r  e  a  l  a  g  e  d  o
g  i  g  u  a  r  d  o  m  a  c
u  o  t  c  a  r  t  o  n  n  o
e  x  n  y  c  e  r  s  h  g  u
s  s  e  e  f  a  c  e  u  e  l
s  a  n  g  i  a  n  t  g  r  d
c  o  a  s  t  q  c  l  e  a  n
```

age
carton
cereal
city
clean
coast
could
danger
face
giant
gone
goose
guard
guess
huge

 Edit Spelling

Mark the misspelled words.
Write them correctly on the lines.

1. age
2. cartun
3. sereal
4. citee
5. clean

6. koast
7. could
8. danjer
9. fase
10. giant

11. gawn
12. goose
13. gard
14. guess
15. huje

_____   _____   _____

_____   _____   _____

_____   _____   _____

Building Spelling Skills

Name:

Word Meaning

Read the phrases.
Draw a picture to show what you read.

a carton of cereal	**a goose's face**	**a huge giant**

Fill in the missing word.

1. The movie star had a _____ to protect her.

2. Have you ever been to New York _____?

3. The warning sign said "_____! Falling rocks."

4. The magician could _____ a person's _____.

5. Did you help _____ up the beach on Saturday?

6. Why does that lady always buy _____-sized packages of everything?

coast	guess	clean
city	guard	gone
age	danger	giant

Building Spelling Skills

Name: _____

Phonics

Read the words and listen to the sounds of the letters *c* and *g*.
Write the words in the correct boxes.

s	k	j	g

age	giant	clean	coast	face
carton	gone	guess	could	goose
cereal	city	huge	danger	guard

Antonyms

Write the antonyms on the line.

giant	gone	city	clean
guess	huge	danger	guard

1. know _____

2. country _____

3. tiny _____

4. safety _____

5. present _____

6. dirty _____

Fill in the missing words.

1. When faced with _____ he ran for _____ .

2. Did you _____ the answer or did you just _____ ?

3. The _____ goat hid from the _____ wolf.

4. Harry was _____ in class this morning, but he is _____ now.

Name:

Spelling List

21

Read and spell	Copy and spell	Spell and check
1. word		
2. work		
3. world		
4. were		
5. first		
6. girl		
7. turned		
8. learn		
9. bird		
10. fire		
11. here		
12. nurse		
13. jury		
14. stirred		
15. wear		
16. _____ *special word*		
17. _____ *special word*		

fold

Building Spelling Skills

Name: _____

Unscramble the words.

1. drow _____
2. rowk _____
3. gril _____
4. laern _____
5. fier _____

6. weer _____
7. nuser _____
8. brid _____
9. rowld _____
10. yurj _____

11. frist _____
12. raew _____
13. ternud _____
14. sterrid _____
15. reeh _____

word	were	turned	fire	jury
work	first	earn	here	stirred
world	girl	bird	nurse	wear

Edit Spelling

Mark the misspelled words.
Write the correct spelling on the lines.

Raul was on his way to wurk when he tirned a corner and saw a house on frie. Ferst he called 911. Then he looked around the house.

Raul herd a gril calling for help. He helped her crawl out of a window.

At the hospital a nerse took good care of the gerl. The child said, "I want to lurn how to be a nurs when I grow up."

_____   _____   _____

_____   _____   _____

_____   _____   _____

                _____

Name:	# Word Meaning

21

Answer the questions.

1. Who helps sick and injured people? _____

2. Which spelling word means...?

   the earth _____

   in this place _____

   mixed it up _____

3. What do you call letters put together to represent something? _____

4. Who decides if a person is innocent or guilty of a crime? _____

5. Circle the meaning of fire in this sentence.

   The nurse was fired from his job.

   a. started to burn

   b. no longer allowed to work there

   c. shot from a cannon

6. Which spelling word is the opposite of...?

   last _____

   play _____

   boy _____

   there _____

word	work	world	were	first
girl	turned	learn	bird	fire
here	nurse	jury	stirred	wear

Write sentences with _____ **and** _____ .

_____

_____

_____

Name:

Word Study

21

Phonics

Circle the letters that say *er* in these words.

1. first
2. learn
3. turned
4. girl
5. word
6. were
7. faster
8. work

Fill in the missing letters.

er	ir	ur	ear	wor

1. n_____se
2. b_____d
3. h_____
4. _____ld
5. l_____n
6. quick_____
7. _____rd
8. st_____red

Rhyming Words

Write the spelling word that rhymes with each numbered word below.

1. care _____
2. fur _____
3. clerk _____
4. burst _____
5. curl _____
6. fern _____
7. bird _____
8. liar _____
9. purse _____

word	work	world	were	first
girl	learn	fire	wear	nurse

Fill in the missing word.

1. What are you going to _____ to the party?
2. Where _____ the boys going in such a hurry?
3. My dad has to _____ in the garden this Saturday.
4. Her mother is a _____ in Dr. Chan's office.

Building Spelling Skills 3-4 EMC 726

Name:

Spelling List

22

Read and spell	Copy and spell	Spell and check
1. aren't		
2. partner		
3. hard		
4. chart		
5. farm		
6. start		
7. large		
8. more		
9. before		
10. horse		
11. north		
12. morning		
13. care		
14. stare		
15. warning		
16. _____		
special word		
17. _____		
special word		

fold

Building Spelling Skills

Name:

Visual Memory

22

Match the parts to make a word.
Write the complete word on the line.

1. far	th	1. _____
2. lar	n't	2. _____
3. nor	m	3. _____
4. are	re	4. _____
5. sta	ge	5. _____
6. warn	fore	6. _____
7. be	ner	7. _____
8. part	ing	8. _____

Edit Spelling

Mark the misspelled words.
Write them on the lines.

1. arent
2. care
3. mor
4. chard
5. farm

6. narth
7. stayr
8. morning
9. befor
10. start

11. horse
12. partnur
13. hard
14. warning
15. larje

_____   _____   _____

_____   _____   _____

_____   _____   _____

©1998 by Evan-Moor Corp.   109   Building Spelling Skills 3-4 EMC 726

Building Spelling Skills

Name: _____

Word Meaning

22

Fill in the missing words.

1. His _____ rode off _____ daybreak.

horse	partner	start	before

2. Is it hard work to run a _____ _____?

more	farm	care	large

3. We must _____ on our trip early in the _____.

morning	before	start	warning

4. Read the _____ on the _____ before you dive off the high board.

morning	warning	start	chart

5. _____ you taking _____ of the sick _____ any more?

Don't	Aren't	horse	care

6. It isn't polite to _____ at people.

care	stare	before

7. The explorer had a _____ trip going by dogsled.

large	more	north	hard

Write sentences with _____ **and** _____ .

_____

_____

_____

_____

Building Spelling Skills

Name: _____

Phonics

Fill in the missing letters to make a word.

| ar | or | are | ore |

1. p_____tner
2. n_____th
3. m_____ning
4. c_____
5. h_____d

6. _____en't
7. bef_____
8. w_____ning
9. st_____
10. l_____ge

11. m_____e
12. ch_____t
13. st_____t
14. h_____se
15. f_____m

Antonyms

Write the opposite of each word on your spelling list.

1. easy _____
2. tiny _____
3. less _____
4. after _____

5. south _____
6. evening _____
7. finish _____

Fill in the missing words.

1. The _____ giant and the _____ elf were friends.

2. I take a walk in the _____ and again in the _____ .

3. Migrating birds fly _____ in the fall and _____ in the spring.

4. I do my homework _____ dinner and then I play _____ dinner.

Name:

Spelling List

23

Read and spell	Copy and spell	Spell and check
1. threw		
2. through		
3. thoughtless		
4. caught		
5. fault		
6. taught		
7. because		
8. one		
9. once		
10. water		
11. watch		
12. wanted		
13. wonder		
14. wonderful		
15. walk		
16. _____ special word		
17. _____ special word		

fold

Building Spelling Skills

Name:

Find the words hiding in this puzzle.

```
w  a  n  t  e  d  e  d  b  e  c
t  h  o  u  g  h  t  l  e  s  s
h  r  t  a  u  g  h  t  c  w  o
r  e  w  a  t  e  r  o  a  o  n
e  w  a  a  n  d  o  o  u  n  c
w  f  a  u  l  t  u  n  s  f  e
w  a  t  c  h  k  g  w  e  u  t
o  n  c  a  u  g  h  t  x  l  e
n  w  o  n  d  e  r  f  u  l  d
```

because
caught
fault
once
one
taught
thoughtless
threw
through
walk
wanted
watch
water
wonderful

Edit Spelling

Mark the misspelled words.
Write them correctly on the lines.

1. wundir
2. caught
3. walck
4. wunce
5. becuz

6. tawght
7. thoughtless
8. watur
9. through
10. fawlt

11. wanted
12. throo
13. wach
14. onederful
15. one

_____

_____

_____

_____

_____

_____

_____

_____

_____

Building Spelling Skills 3-4 EMC 726

Name:	# Word Meaning

23

Answer the questions.

1. Which word belongs in each sentence?   **threw   through**

The fox ran _____ a hole in the fence.

Someone _____ a pie in the clown's face.

2. Which spelling words rhyme with...?

bought   _____   _____

new   _____   _____

3. Which meaning does watch have in this sentence?

You must **watch** your step when you climb a ladder.

    a. be careful

    b. something that tells time

    c. standing guard

4. Which word means "only one time"? _____

5. Which word means "very special"? _____

6. What is the past tense of...?   catch _____   teach _____

throw _____   want _____

threw	walk	one	through	wonderful
once	water	wonder	watch	thoughtless
caught	wanted	because	fault	taught

Write sentences with _____ **and** _____ .

_____

_____

_____

       Building Spelling Skills 3-4 EMC 726

Building Spelling Skills

Name: _____

Word Study

Phonics

Read the words. Write them in the correct boxes.

the sound of **wu** in **won**	the sound of **wa** in **wall**	the sound of **aw** in **fawn**	the sound of **oo** in **too**	
wanted	water	caught	watch	walk
threw	one	wonderful	wonder	taught
thought	because	through	fault	once

Structure

Add the correct suffix to the words.

less means **without**
ful means **filled with**

1. Morris had a _____ surprise.
   (wonder)

2. It was _____ of you to be late for the party.
   (thought)

3. The _____ man helped fix the flat tire.
   (thought)

4. I always feel _____ on my birthday.
   (joy)

5. A newborn kitten is _____.
   (help)

6. Will you be _____ and clean up that mess?
   (help)

Name:

Spelling List

24

Read and spell	Copy and spell	Spell and check
1. color		
2. odor		
3. store		
4. calendar		
5. dollar		
6. party		
7. liar		
8. after		
9. number		
10. better		
11. doctor		
12. weather		
13. every		
14. forty		
15. sugar		
16. _____ *special word*		
17. _____ *special word*		

fold

Building Spelling Skills

Name: _____

Match the parts.
Write the words on the lines.

1. co	y	1.	_____
2. calen	ber	2.	_____
3. part	lor	3.	_____
4. ev	dar	4.	_____
5. num	ery	5.	_____
6. o	gar	6.	_____
7. doc	dor	7.	_____
8. for	tor	8.	_____
9. su	ty	9.	_____
10. weath	ter	10.	_____
11. li	ter	11.	_____
12. bet	ar	12.	_____
13. af	er	13.	_____

Edit Spelling

Correct the misspelled words.

1. The calender cost one doller.

   _____ _____

2. Dad had a big partie when he turned fourty.

   _____ _____

3. You had bettir see the doctur about that bad cold.

   _____ _____

4. What nummer comes after nine?

   _____

5. Evry flower in the garden has a sweet oder.

   _____ _____

Building Spelling Skills

Name:	**Word Meaning**	24

Answer these questions.

1. Which letters make the sound er in these words?

   liar _____   after _____   doctor _____

2. What sound does the final y make in these words: forty, every, party? _____

3. What do you call someone who helps sick people to feel better? _____

4. What do you call someone who is not truthful? _____

5. What does a calendar tell you? _____

6. Which spelling word has the sound of sh in she? _____

7. Which spelling word means all? _____

8. What is the opposite of...?   before _____

                                    worse _____

color	odor	store	dollar	calendar
party	liar	after	number	better
doctor	weather	every	sugar	forty

Write sentences with _____ **and** _____ .

_____

_____

_____

_____

                                         Building Spelling Skills 3-4 EMC 726

Name:

Phonics

Underline all the words that have the sound of _er_ in her.
Circle the letters that make the _er_ sound.

color	every	better
odor	calendar	sugar
dollar	watch	stare
march	number	liar
store	weather	after

Structure

Divide the words into syllables.

1. color   co lor
2. calendar   _____
3. better   _____
4. every   _____
5. store   _____
6. number   _____

7. party   _____
8. liar   _____
9. weather   _____
10. odor   _____
11. after   _____
12. sugar   _____

Name: _____

Spelling List

25

Read and spell	Copy and spell	Spell and check
1. phone		
2. photograph		
3. orphan		
4. alphabet		
5. graph		
6. nephew		
7. enough		
8. father		
9. half		
10. Friday		
11. cough		
12. unhappy		
13. happier		
14. happily		
15. happiness		
16. _____ special word		
17. _____ special word		

fold

Name:

Match the parts to make words.
Write the complete word on the line.

1. Fri   phan   1. _____
2. fa   ew   2. _____
3. or   day   3. _____
4. neph   nough   4. _____
5. e   ther   5. _____
6. pho   pi   py   6. _____
7. al   hap   bet   7. _____
8. un   to   graph 8. _____
9. hap   pha   ly   9. _____

Edit Spelling

Mark the misspelled words.
Write them correctly on the lines.

1. fone   5. fotograph   9. orfan
2. haf   6. fadder   10. happiness
3. alfabet   7. nefew   11. enuf
4. cough   8. graph   12. Fritay

_____   _____   _____

_____   _____   _____

_____   _____   _____

| Name: | **Word Meaning** | ⭐ 25 |

Answer the questions.

1. What do you call a picture taken with a camera? _____

2. What is the word for a child whose parents are dead? _____

3. What is a name for all the letters from a to z? _____

4. Which spelling word means "all I need"? _____

5. What do you do when you have a bad cold? _____

6. Which spelling words are names for family members?

   _____   _____

7. Which of these words rhyme?

   enough   cough   stuff

8. Which words have three syllables?

   Friday   photograph   alphabet

phone	orphan	nephew	happiness	cough
alphabet	graph	enough	Friday	photograph
father	half	unhappy	happier	happily

Write sentences with _____ **and** _____ **.**

_____

_____

_____

Building Spelling Skills

Name:	**Word Study**	⭐25

Phonics

f	ph	gh

Fill in the missing letters.

1. _____one
2. enou_____
3. or_____an
4. _____ather
5. _____riday

6. ne_____ew
7. hal_____
8. gra_____
9. al_____abet
10. _____otogra_____

1. Grandmother has an old ph_____ of her mother.

2. The first grade teacher wrote the _____ph_____ on the chalkboard.

3. Give _____f of the chicken to F_____.

Structure

ly - quickly
ness - goodness

Change words by adding a suffix.

1. She climbed _____ and _____ to the top of the tree.
   (slow)   (careful)

2. The explorers were surrounded by _____ inside the cave.
                                        (dark)

3. Red Riding Hood skipped along _____ to Grandma's house.
                                      (happy)

4. His _____ filled my heart with _____.
      (kind)   (happy)

Building Spelling Skills

Name:

Read and spell	Copy and spell	Spell and check
1. ghost		
2. neighbor		
3. high		
4. knew		
5. knot		
6. unknown		
7. rewrap		
8. wrong		
9. written		
10. wrapper		
11. unwrap		
12. climb		
13. limb		
14. gnaw		
15. gnat		
16. _____ special word		
17. _____ special word		

fold

Building Spelling Skills

Name:

Visual Memory

Find the spelling words hiding in this puzzle.

g	h	o	s	t	k	n	e	w	z
n	e	i	g	h	g	o	r	r	w
k	x	g	g	i	r	l	e	i	r
n	w	n	n	h	k	i	w	t	a
o	r	o	a	a	g	m	r	t	p
t	o	t	t	s	w	b	a	e	p
u	n	k	n	o	w	n	p	n	e
o	g	u	m	c	l	i	m	b	r
i	n	u	n	w	r	a	p	g	o

climb
ghost
gnat
gnaw
high
knew
knot
limb
neighbor
rewrap
unknown
unwrap
wrapper
written
wrong

Edit Spelling

Mark the misspelled words.
Write them correctly on the lines.

gost	gnat	enwrap
naybor	unknone	clim
hi	rewrap	limb
knoo	rong	naw
knot	written	

_____ _____ _____

_____ _____ _____

_____ _____ _____

1. The ribbon was tied in a not. _____

2. Little nats flew around the fruit tree. _____

3. A lim broke off the tree in the storm. _____

Name:

Word Meaning

26

Complete the crossword puzzle.

Across

1. not known

4. to move up a ladder

6. take off the covering

8. spirit of someone dead seen by a person

9. a fastening made by tying string together

Down

2. person who lives next door

3. opposite of right

5. words were put on paper

7. small insect

8. chew on

ghost	unknown
high	rewrap
gnaw	wrong
limb	unwrap
knew	climb
written	gnat
knot	neighbor

Building Spelling Skills

Name: _____

Word Study

Phonics

Put an x over the silent letters.

x̶wrap	x̶knot

ghost	knew	wrong
high	write	unwrap
gnaw	knot	climb
limb	unknown	gnat

Structure

Put a prefix in front of each word.

un - unhappy
re - recall

1. My cat tore the paper on the gift so Mother had to _____ it.
   (wrap)

2. The name of the artist was _____.
   (known)

3. People were _____ of what to do after the earthquake.
   (sure)

4. My homework paper was messy so I had to _____ it.
   (write)

5. _____ the present to see what is inside.
   (Wrap)

6. Uncle Ted must _____ the fence every five years.
   (paint)

 Building Spelling Skills 3-4 EMC 726

Name:

Spelling List

27

Read and spell	Copy and spell	Spell and check
1. useful		
2. quietly		
3. slowly		
4. careful		
5. careless		
6. quickly		
7. useless		
8. worthless		
9. fearful		
10. fearless		
11. joyful		
12. smarter		
13. fastest		
14. funniest		
15. happiest		
16. _____		
special word		
17. _____		
special word		

fold

Name:

Visual Memory

27

What suffix is missing?

ful	ly	less	er

1. use _____

2. use _____

3. quiet _____

4. worth _____

5. smart _____

6. slow _____

7. joy _____

8. fast _____

9. care_____

10. care _____

11. fear _____

12. fear _____

 Edit Spelling

Mark the misspelled words.
Write them correctly on the lines.

1. Mother walked slooly and kwietly past the sleeping baby.

_____ _____

2. Carla was joyfull when she won the race as the fastist runner in school.

_____ _____

3. It is useles to do the job if you are kareless.

_____ _____

4. Pete is the happyest person I know.

_____

5. A feerless shepherd quikly chased away the hungry wolf.

_____ _____

Building Spelling Skills

Name: _____

Word Meaning

27

Answer the questions.

1. What do these words do?

   smarter faster

   a. name something
   b. compare something
   c. describe something

2. What do these words do?

   funniest   thoughtless   useful

   a. name something
   b. compare something
   c. describe something

3. Which spelling word is the opposite of...?

   quickly _____

   useful _____

   careless _____

   saddest _____

4. What word means "afraid"? _____

5. Which word describes someone who always makes
   messes and breaks things? _____

useful	quietly	slowly	careful	quickly
careless	useless	fearful	joyful	worthless
smarter	faster	fearless	funniest	happiest

Write sentences with _____ **and** _____ .

_____

_____

_____

_____

Name:

Word Study

27

Structure

Add the suffix *est* to these words. Mark what you did to change the word.	no change	double final consonant	change y to i and add est
1. fast ___fastest___	✓		
2. happy _____			
3. quick _____			
4. funny _____			
5. sad _____			
6. big _____			
7. smart _____			
8. silly _____			

Add suffixes to words to complete the sentences.

ful   less

1. Be care_____ as you work so you don't make a care_____ mistake.

2. The fear_____ firefighter rescued the fear_____ boy from the wrecked car.

3. Throw away the use_____ trash, recycle things that are still use_____.

er   est

1. Roy can run fast_____ than me, but Stan is the fast_____ runner.

2. I know a snail is slow_____ than a turtle, but what animal is the slow_____ of all?

3. That geography test was the hard_____ test I ever took. I think it was even hard_____ than our math test.

Name:

Spelling List

28

Read and spell	Copy and spell	Spell and check
1. brother		
2. mother		
3. another		
4. field		
5. friend		
6. heard		
7. early		
8. friendly		
9. head		
10. near		
11. year		
12. shield		
13. eat		
14. measure		
15. break		
16. _____ special word		
17. _____ special word		

fold

Name:

Visual Memory

28

Find the words hiding in this puzzle.

```
m  e  a  s  u  r  e  e  a  a
o  n  e  h  e  a  r  d  n  n
t  r  y  i  e  l  f  s  o  b
h  x  n  e  n  d  i  e  t  r
e  e  e  l  a  h  e  a  h  e
r  a  a  d  o  r  l  r  e  a
n  t  r  d  e  a  d  l  r  k
f  r  i  e  n  d  l  y  o  r
a  n  o  b  r  o  t  h  e  r
```

another
break
brother
early
eat
field
friendly
head
heard
measure
mother
near
shield
year

Edit Spelling

Mark the misspelled words.
Write the correct spelling on the lines.

1. My muther and bruther have the same birthday.

   _____   _____

2. Trina hurd from an old frend today.

   _____   _____

3. We herd a noise in the empty feeld next door.

   _____   _____

4. Erly next yeer they are moving to Texas.

   _____   _____

5. May I eta unother slice of pie?

   _____   _____

Name:

Complete the crossword puzzle.

Across

3. opposite of sister
4. chew and swallow food
6. find the size of something
7. listened to
8. January 1 to December 31
10. open area with few trees
11. a female parent

Down

1. piece of armor
2. a person who knows and likes another person
3. smash
4. opposite of late
5. moved around; rotated
7. the top part of your body
9. close by

break	measure
brother	mother
early	near
field	shield
friend	turned
head	year
heard	eat

Building Spelling Skills

Word Study

28

Phonics

Write the words in the correct boxes.

sound of long e	sound of long a	sound of short e	schwa

another   eat   measure   near

break   field   mother   shield

brother   head   year

Phonics

Change the beginning sounds to create new words.

_____other   _____ead   _____eat   _____ear

_____other   _____ead   _____eat   _____ear

_____other   _____ead   _____eat   _____ear

_____other   _____ead   _____eat   _____ear

Name:

Spelling List

29

Read and spell	Copy and spell	Spell and check
1. war		
2. word		
3. their		
4. there		
5. night		
6. knight		
7. right		
8. write		
9. weight		
10. wait		
11. piece		
12. peace		
13. hour		
14. our		
15. wrote		
16. _____ special word		
17. _____ special word		

fold

Building Spelling Skills

Name:

Match the scrambled word to the correct word.

1. raw	their	7. twai	right
2. drow	word	8. peice	wait
3. threi	there	9. rou	piece
4. heret	war	10. hour	wrote
5. ightn	write	11. ritgh	hour
6. ritwe	night	12. rwote	our

 Edit Spelling

Mark the misspelled words.
Write them correctly on the lines.

1. Put the box rite over their.

   _____ _____

2. The brave night saved a princess last nite.

   _____ _____

3. Mom said to weight here for an howr.

   _____ _____

4. Hour friends came to dinner last nitgh.

   _____ _____

5. May I have a peace of there pizza?

   _____ _____

6. How do you right the first werd of your name?

   _____ _____

Building Spelling Skills

Name:

Word Meaning

Fill in the missing words.

1. Can you put _____ coats in the closet over _____?

   their   there   they're

2. The _____'s fight with the fierce dragon lasted all

   _____ long.

   night   might   knight

3. Try to _____ the spelling word _____ this time.

   white   right   write

4. Every Friday after school we spend an _____ with

   _____ grandfather.

   our   flour   hour

5. What is the _____ of that huge hog?

   wait   write   weight

6. That _____ of paper is a _____ treaty.

   piece   price   peace

7. Who _____ that song?

   rot   write   wrote

Write sentences with _____ and _____ .

_____

_____

_____

Building Spelling Skills

Name: _____

Word Study

Phonics

Write the words in the correct boxes by long vowel sounds.
Circle the letters that spell the sounds.

long a	long i	long e

weight   night   peace   right   plane   site
piece   wait   write   beach   stair   beech
flee   knight   plain   sight   flea   stare

Opposites

Write the opposite.

1. erase _____
2. day _____
3. here _____
4. left _____

5. war _____
6. leave _____
7. whole _____
8. your _____

Fill in the missing word.

1. If you _____ the word wrong, _____ it and try again.

2. I'm going to _____ for the bus to come, but you

   may _____ if you need to go.

3. The generals signed the _____ treaty to end the _____.

Name:

Spelling List

30

Read and spell	Copy and spell	Spell and check
1. air		
2. against		
3. all right		
4. until		
5. presents		
6. beautiful		
7. favorite		
8. clothes		
9. people		
10. vacation		
11. remember		
12. already		
13. hospital		
14. minute		
15. straight		
16. _____ special word		
17. _____ special word		

fold

Building Spelling Skills

Visual Memory

30

Match the parts to make words.
Write the complete word on the line.

1. a   sents
2. un   ute
3. pre   gainst
4. peo   til
5. min   ple
6. beau   ca   ber
7. va   read   ful
8. re   ti   al
9. al   pit   y
10. hos   mem   tion

1. _____
2. _____
3. _____
4. _____
5. _____
6. _____
7. _____
8. _____
9. _____
10. _____

Edit Spelling

Mark the misspelled words.
Write them correctly on the lines.

air   bootiful   already
alright   favrute   remimber
until   clothes   hospitul
against   peeple   minite
presunts   vacashun   strate

_____   _____   _____

_____   _____   _____

_____   _____   _____

_____

Building Spelling Skills

Word Meaning

30

Complete the crossword puzzle.

Across

4. gifts
7. a time of rest from school or work
8. what people wear
9. happened before this time
10. don't forget
12. opposite of for

Down

1. place for the care of the sick or injured
2. not crooked
3. very pretty
5. men, women, and children
6. the one you like best
11. there are 60 of these in an hour

against	clothes	minute	remember
already	favorite	people	straight
beautiful	hospital	presents	vacation

Building Spelling Skills 3-4 EMC 726

Building Spelling Skills

Name:

Word Study

30

Phonics

Circle the letters in the word that represent the sound given.

long a – f(a)vorite

short e – remember

long a – straight

schwa – hospital

long e – already

short i – minute

long a – vacation

short i – until

schwa – against

long i – all right

short u – until

long o – clothes

long e – people

Structure

Divide the word into syllables.
Write the number of syllables in the word on the line.

1. against   a gainst   2

2. presents _____ ___

3. beautiful _____ ___

4. air _____ ___

5. favorite _____ ___

6. clothes _____ ___

7. people _____ ___

8. vacation _____ ___

9. minute _____ ___

10. straight _____ ___

11. hospital _____ ___

12. already _____ ___

13. remember _____ ___

14. until _____ ___

©1998 by Evan-Moor Corp.   143   Building Spelling Skills 3-4 EMC 726

Spelling Checklist

Spelling List Number	Student Names															
1																
2																
3																
4																
5																
6																
7																
8																
9																
10																
11																
12																
13																
14																
15																
16																
17																
18																
19																
20																
21																
22																
23																
24																
25																
26																
27																
28																
29																
30																

 Building Spelling Skills 3-4 EMC 726

Individual Spelling Record

Date	Spelling List	Number Correct	Words Missed	Comments

Building Spelling Skills 3-4 EMC 726

Name:

Spelling

1. _____
2. _____
3. _____
4. _____
5. _____
6. _____
7. _____
8. _____
9. _____

10. _____
11. _____
12. _____
13. _____
14. _____
15. _____
16. _____
17. _____

Review Words

1. _____   2. _____   3. _____

 ## Sentence Dictation

1. _____

_____

2. _____

_____

3. _____

_____

Note: Reproduce this page to make your own spelling lists.

Name:

Spelling List

Read and spell	Copy and spell	Spell and check
1.	_____	_____
2.	_____	_____
3.	_____	_____
4.	_____	_____
5.	_____	_____
6.	_____	_____
7.	_____	_____
8.	_____	_____
9.	_____	_____
10.	_____	_____
11.	_____	_____
12.	_____	_____
13.	_____	_____
14.	_____	_____
15.	_____	_____
16. _____	_____	_____
special word		
17. _____	_____	_____
special word		

fold

Building Spelling Skills

Note: Reproduce this page to make your own configuration puzzles.

Name:

Note: Reproduce this page to make your own sorting activities.

Name:

Word Sort

Read the words.
Write them in the boxes.

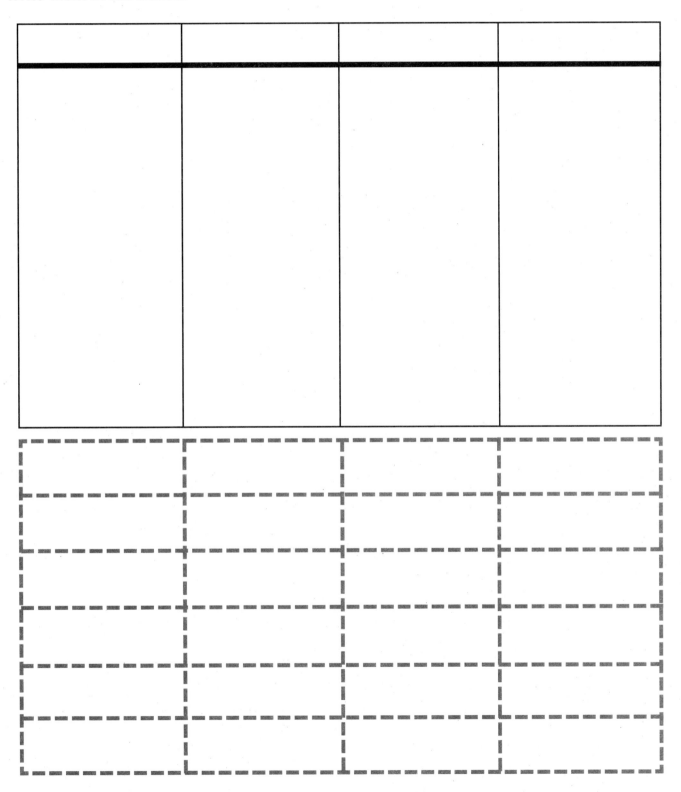

Note: Reproduce this letter to send home with spelling lists.

Dear Parents,

Attached is your child's spelling list for this week. Encourage him/her to practice the words in one or more of these ways.

1. Read and spell each word. Cover it up and write it. Uncover the word and check to see if it is correct.

2. Find the words on the spelling list in printed materials such as books and magazines.

3. You read a word aloud and ask your child to spell it (either aloud or written on paper).

Thank you for your support of our spelling program.

Sincerely,

Dear Parents,

Attached is your child's spelling list for this week. Encourage him/her to practice the words in one or more of these ways.

1. Read and spell each word. Cover it up and write it. Uncover the word and check to see if it is correct.

2. Find the words on the spelling list in printed materials such as books and magazines.

3. You read a word aloud and ask your child to spell it (either aloud or written on paper).

Thank you for your support of our spelling program.

Sincerely,

Answer Key

Page 25
1. afraid 2. eight 3. away 4. ask
5. great 6. takes 7. than 8. said
9. always 10. they 11. catch
12. prey

1. sed	8. thay
2. eitgh	9. aks
3. grait	10. stend
4. drey	11. paling
5. catsh	12. taks
6. ufraid	13. fhan
7. wavd	14. uway

Page 26
1. eight	prey
2. takes	catch
3. always	afraid
4. They	playing
5. waved	said
6. stand	away
7. ask	great

Sentences will vary.

Page 27
wave catch away takes great
ask eight stand said they
always afraid prey than playing

1. played playing
2. asked asking
3. preyed preying
4. painted painting

1. waved waving
2. smiled smiling
3. skated skating
4. baked baking

Page 29
1. between or believe 2. leave
3. easy or many or very
4. easy or many or very
5. please 6. three 7. help
8. she 9. believe or between
10. easy or many or very
11. seen 12. next

These words should be marked.
Correct spelling is underlined.

1. Plez	Please
2. leaf	leave
3. eezy	easy
4. ben	been
5. betwene	between
6. belive	believe
7. miny	many
8. tree	three

Page 30
1. b
2. sea
3. a. easy
   b. left
   c. she
   d. many
   e. leave
4. between
5. please
6. believe
Sentences will vary.

Page 31
three left she
please believe many
very been seen
help between leave
easy sea next

1. very   6. sea, she, or
2. many   three
3. please   7. seen
4. sea, she, 8. believe
   or three   9. sea, she, or
5. help   three
              10. between

Page 33
1. while 2. buy or try 3. light
4. my 5. life 6. swim 7. which
8. eye 9. drink 10. pitch
11. kind or find 12. why

These words should be marked.
Correct spelling is underlined.

1. bie lite	buy	light
2. Witch drenk	Which	drink
3. Trie picth	Try	pitch
4. swem aye	swim	eye
5. Eye by	I	buy

Page 34
1. I	eye	
2. Why	buy	drink
3. Swim	try	find
4. Which	light	
5. while	pitch	
6. my	try	
7. kind	life	

Page 35
life	drink	try
pitch	while	I
my	light	buy
eye	which	find
why	kind	swim

Answers will vary but could include:

find	file	might	link
bind	mile	light	pink
blind	pile	bright	wink
mind	tile	fight	rink
rind	smile	sight	drink
wind	while	tight	think

Page 37
1. pocket 2. almost 3. coach
4. open 5. often 6. grow 7. most
8. also 9. throne 10. hold/told/
both
11. rocket 12. sew

1. roket	7. koach
2. whold	8. allso
3. offen	9. opun
4. thone	10. groe
5. amolst	11. tole
6. bofh	12. sowe

Page 38
1. throne
2. pocket
3. told, hold
4. coach
5. so, sew
6. open
7. rocket
8. sew
Sentences will vary.

Page 39

rocket	hold	throne
grow	so	pocket
told	also	sew
most	often	almost
both	coach	open

1. grow
2. told
3. hold
4. so
5. sew
6. both
7. coach
8. throne
9. most

1. rocket
2. also
3. often
4. pocket
5. open
6. almost

Page 41
1. much
2. touch
3. use
4. you
5. unit
6. few
7. fuel
8. under
9. such
10. human
11. music
12. young

These words should be marked.
Correct spelling is underlined.
1. undar — under
2. noo — new
3. yer — your
4. kute — cute
5. tuch — touch
6. yung — young
7. fuo — few
8. moosic — music

Page 42
Pictures will vary but must reflect sentence meaning.

Page 43

use	such	few
young	music	under
your	you	unit
cute	much	new
fuel	human	touch

1. much, such or touch
2. young
3. under
4. use
5. few or new or you
6. cute
7. new or few or you
8. fuel
9. such or much or touch
10. your

1. under — thunder
2. few — new
3. cute — flute

Page 45

too	alike	blew	know
blue	two	to	do
above	move	save	have
give	live	alive	

These words should be marked.
Correct spellings are underlined.
1. tow — two
2. ulike — alike
3. blew — blue
4. no — know
5. hav — have
6. geve — give
7. too — to
8. Moov — Move

Page 46
1. two
2. too
3. to
1. blew
2. blue
1. know
2. no
Sentences will vary.

Page 47
short vowel   above have live give
long vowel   know save
sound of o in to

blew	move
blue	too
do	two

1. gave
2. moved
3. lived
4. knew
5. blew
6. did
7. had
8. saved

1. moved
2. know
3. blew
4. saved

Page 49

These words should be circled.
1. missed
2. balloon
3. pretty
4. letter
5. different
6. pattern
7. carry
8. off
9. zipper

Page 50
1. spelling
2. Mississippi
3. balloon
4. zipper
5. carry
6. letter
7. different
8. pattern
Sentences will vary.

Page 51
1. t ed d
2. carry pretty
3. spell - no change
   carry - change y to i, add ed

1. miss ing
2. bal loon
3. spell ing
4. pret ty
5. add ed
6. let ter
7. mid dle
8. will ing
9. zip per
10. car ry
11. pat tern
12. dif fer ent

Page 53
1. mm
2. m
3. tt
4. t
5. d
6. pp
7. l
8. ll
9. m
10. m
11. k
12. v

1. swimming
2. getting
3. coming
4. having
5. doing
6. happened
7. happening
8. joked
9. smiled
10. came

1. started
2. received
3. smiling

Page 54
1. swam
   swimming
2. happening
   happened
3. coming
   came
4. smiled
   smiling
Sentences will vary.

Page 55
1. joked
2. swam
3. happened
4. ended
5. came
6. did
7. smiled
8. had
9. received
10. hid
11. called
12. flew

---

1. swimming - double
2. getting - double
3. receiving - drop e
4. coming - drop e
5. having - drop e
6. doing - no change
7. smiling - drop e
8. ending - no change
9. happening - no change
10. starting - no change
11. joking - drop e

Page 57
yaw — way
thees — these
neice — niece
hows — show
anme — mean
locse — close
deirt — tried

beuc — cube
ripce — price
mitgh — might
foalt — float
niarb — brain
formuni — uniform
edstay — stayed

1. youniform — uniform
2. Cloze — close
3. mite — might
4. kube — cube
5. staid — stayed
6. tryed — tried
7. shoo — show
8. flote — float

Page 58
Across
1. mean
4. price
5. uniform
8. close
9. these

Down
2. niece
3. brain
6. float
7. cube
10. stay

Page 59
1. a
2. e
3. e
4. o
5. o
6. a
7. e
8. o
9. i
10. u
11. u
12. a
13. i
Bonus-u u e

1. stayed-no change
2. tried-y to i
3. floated-no change
4. showed-no change
5. cried-y to i
6. hurried-y to i
7. planted-no change
8. worried-y to i

1. baked
2. scurried
3. burrowed

Page 61
1. search
2. finish
3. think
4. short
5. whole
6. with
7. where
8. children
9. together
10. teacher
11. everywhere
12. reached

These words should be marked.
Correct spellings are underlined.
1. Hoo htat hole
   who that whole
2. childrun poosh
   children push
3. finnish shirt
   finish short
4. tink serch
   think search
5. teecher togepher
   teacher together

Page 62
1. teacher, children
2. everywhere
3. think
4. finish
5. search
6. whole
   short
   together
7. new, who, shoe
8. show, sure
Sentences ill vary.

Page 63

1. <u>ch</u>ildren   7. to<u>ge</u>ther
2. sear<u>ch</u>   8. pu<u>sh</u>
3. <u>th</u>ink   9. tea<u>ch</u>er
4. <u>wh</u>ole   10. wi<u>th</u>
5. <u>wh</u>ere   11. <u>sh</u>ort
6. fini<u>sh</u>   12. <u>wh</u>o

1. 3   9. 1
2. 1   10. 2
3. 1   11. 1
4. 2   12. 2
5. 1   13. 1
6. 1   14. 1
7. 1   15. 1
8. 3

Page 65

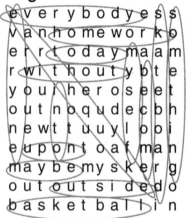

These words should be marked.
Correct spellings are underlined.
homewerk   <u>homework</u>
misef   <u>myself</u>
owtside   <u>outside</u>
skatbord   <u>skateboard</u>
Everbody   <u>Everybody</u>
baskutball   <u>basketball</u>

Evrywon   <u>Everyone</u>
sumthing   <u>something</u>
erthquak   <u>earthquake</u>
wifout   <u>without</u>
Maybee   <u>Maybe</u>

Page 66
1. basketball   skateboard

2. earthquake outside
3. homework   today
4. Something   into
5. upon
6. become
7. without
8. Everyone or Everybody
   myself
Sentences will vary.

Page 67
1. into
2. today
3. without
4. something
5. become
6. upon
7. maybe
8. outside
9. basketball
10. homework

1. basket<u>ball</u>   9. <u>maybe</u>
2. be<u>come</u>   10. outside
3. earth<u>quake</u>   11. skate<u>board</u>
4. every<u>body</u>   12. some<u>thing</u>
5. <u>every</u>one   13. to<u>day</u>
6. <u>homework</u>   14. <u>upon</u>
7. in<u>to</u>   15. <u>without</u>
8. <u>my</u>self

Page 69
1. awful   7. rough
2. called   8. longer
3. mall   9. straw
4. song   10. drawing
5. small   11. strongest
6. along   12. falling

These words should be marked.
Correct spelling is underlined.
1. ahful   <u>awful</u>
2. smal starw   <u>small</u> <u>straw</u>
3. drawn stronust   <u>drawing</u>
   <u>strongest</u>
4. bawght moll   <u>bought</u> <u>mall</u>
5. longar sogn   <u>longer</u> <u>song</u>

Page 70
1. awful
2. straw
3. mall

4. drawing
5. tough-stuff-rough
6. bought
   small
   rough
   longer
   strongest
7. b
Sentences will vary.

Page 71
awful   called   tough
mall   song   along
rough   bought   straw
strongest   falling   brought
small   drawing   longer

1. stronger   strongest
2. longer   longest
3. smaller   smallest
4. rougher   roughest
5. tougher   toughest

1. strongest
2. smaller
3. roughest
4. toughest
5. longer

Page 73
1. la<u>dy</u>   6. stud<u>y</u>
2. <u>family</u>   7. fi<u>nally</u>
3. on<u>ly</u>   8. <u>story</u>
4. <u>surprises</u>   9. <u>studied</u>
5. <u>la</u>dies   10. sur<u>prise</u>

These words should be marked.
Correct spellings are underlined.
1. suprise   <u>surprise</u>
2. shoos   <u>shoes</u>
3. cryed   <u>cried</u>
4. famuly   <u>family</u>
5. ladys   <u>ladies</u>
6. storie   <u>story</u>
7. finelly   <u>finally</u>
8. studyed   <u>studied</u>

Page 74
1. surprise
2. ladies
3. finally
4. study
5. shy
6. family
7. surprises
8. cried
Sentences will vary.

Page 75

y says i	y says e
cry	lady
shy	study
why	only
fly	story
my	family
try	funny

Note: Some children find the idea of dropping *silent e* before adding *es* confusing. You may choose to accept "add s" as correct answers for numbers 4 and 7.

1. ladies - y to i, add es
2. toys - add s
3. stories - y to i, add es
4. shoes - drop e, add es
5. families - y to i, add es
6. rockets - add s
7. nieces - drop e, add es

1. ladies
2. story
3. nieces

Page 77

```
f  q  t  r  u  t  h  c  h  f
l  o  o  k  e  d  r  o  c  u
f  o  o  d  o  o  k  o  o  l
t  d  p  t  c  h  e  w  o  l
r  u  u  b  r  o  o  k  m  m
u  e  s  p  a  t  h  i  h  h
e  s  c  h  o  o  l  x  e  e
n  o  s  t  o  o  d  i  m  w
```

Correct spelling underlined.

luked	looked
futbal	football
cookee	cookie
fud	food
poot	put

schol	school
deu	due
troo	true
ruum	room

Page 78

Across	Down
1. food	1. full
3. football	2. cookie
7. brook	4. truth
9. chew	5. looked
10. good	6. true
	8. school

Page 79

u in push	o in do
1. looked	1. food
2. good	2. school
3. brook	3. truth
4. football	4. room
5. cookie	5. true
6. stood	6. chew
7. full	7. due
8. put	

1. full	4. put
2. good	5. truth
3. stood	6. true

1. full
2. put
3. stood

Page 81

yoil — voice
cevoi — oily
soyter — boy
joyen — voyage
yob — oyster
agevoy — loyal
loyla — enjoy

ocin — coin
ingpoint — joined
cocholate — choice
edjoin — chocolate
oichce — pointing
sonpoi — destroy
troydes — poison

These words should be marked.
Correct spellings are underlined.
1. choyse chocklate
   choice   chocolate
2. injoy voyege
   enjoy   voyage
3. distroy poisen
   destroy   poison

4. doy oister
   boy   oyster
5. coyn chose
   coin   choose

Page 82
1. oysters   voyage
2. Chocolate choice
3. boy   destroy
4. pointing   coin
5. voice
6. poison
7. enjoy   loyal
Sentences will vary.

Page 83
boy   oyster   poison   coin

1. oily	5. pointing
2. choice	6. destroy
3. voice	7. enjoy
4. loyal	8. joined

1. points	pointed	pointing
2. joins	joined	joining
3. smiles	smiled	smiling
4. finishes	finished	finishing

1. smiling
2. points
3. finishes
4. joining

Page 85
1. don't	7. let's
2. didn't	8. they're
3. I'll	9. we're
4. that's	10. doesn't
5. it's	11. o'clock
6. can't	12. won't

These words should be marked.
Correct spellings are underlined.

1. din't	didn't
2. were	we're
3. duzn't	doesn't
4. Their	They're
5. Tat's	That's
6. Its	It's
7. kan't	can't
8. A'll	I'll

Page 86

Across	Down
3. o'clock	1. don't
6. doesn't	2. I'll
7. won't	4. can't
8. wouldn't	5. let's
10. they're	6. didn't
11. it's	8. we're
	9. that's

Page 87

1. will not
   do not
2. its
3. 's - is, us
   n't - not
   're - are
4. I'll

	contraction	missing
1.	don't	o
2.	we're	a
3.	they're	a
4.	it's	i
5.	wouldn't	o
6.	can't	no
7.	I'm	a
8.	that's	i
9.	doesn't	o
10.	didn't	o
11.	I'll	wi
12.	let's	u

Page 89

1. town   6. cousin   11. around
2. house   7. about   12. grown
3. group   8. own   13. country
4. found   9. below   14. should
5. follow   10. would   15. ground

These words should be marked.
Correct spellings are underlined.

kussin	cousin
grup	group
toun	town
fallowed	followed
bello	below
arownd	around
groun	ground
cuzin's	cousin's
howse	house

Page 90

1. town   ground
2. cousin   country
3. group   house
4. should   grown
5. Would   follow
6. found   below
7. around
8. own

Sentences will vary.

Page 91

o in go	ow in cow
grown	found
below	town
follow	about
own	around

oo in too	u in up	u in put
group	country	would
soup	cousin	should
		could

1. town
2. about
3. house
4. cousin
5. group
6. should   would
7. follow   below
8. around   found
9. own   grown

Page 93

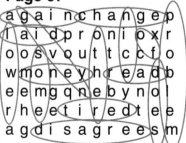

1. A   ver
2. e   pril
3. ba   ny
4. si   u
5. o   bies
6. hell   ven
7. ti   lent
8. men   ture
9. fu   o

1. April
2. even
3. babies
4. silent
5. over
6. hello
7. tiny
8. menu
9. future

These words should be marked.
Correct spellings are underlined.
1. babys deer babies dear
2. raize tiney raise tiny
3. sylent heloo silent hello
4. Aprul whyte April white
5. yousd thoze used those

Page 94

1. menu
2. future
   over
   used
   hello
   silent
3. tiny white babies
4. Change the y to i and add es.
5. April
Sentences will vary.

Page 95

Long a	Long o	Long e
raised	over	even
April	those	dear
	hello	we

Long i	Long u
silent	used
white	future
	menu

1. Ⓐ pril
2. ⓑⓐ bies
3. ⓞ ver
4. hel ⓛⓞ
5. ⓔ ven
6. ⓛⓐ dy
7. ⓢⓘ lent
8. ⓣⓘ ny
9. men ⓤ
10. ⓕⓤ ture
Bonus: ⓥⓐ ⓒⓐ tion

Page 97

a g a i n c h a n g e p
l a i d p r o n i o x r
o o s v o u t t c c f o
w m o n e y h r e a d b
e e m g q n e b y n o l
r h e e t i r e d t e e
a g d i s a g r e e s m

These words should be marked.
Correct spellings are underlined.

prblum	problem
red	read
nyce	nice
picke	picked
muney	money

write	<u>right</u>
chanje	<u>change</u>
monny	<u>money</u>
agin	<u>again</u>
rite	<u>right</u>
mony	<u>money</u>
reed	<u>read</u>

Page 98
1. Does money
2. nice problem
3. disagree read
4. tired change
5. laid of
6. lower again
7. given
8. some
Sentences will vary.

Page 99
1. <u>disagree</u>   6. tired   11. <u>problem</u>
2. <u>again</u>   7. <u>given</u>   12. <u>some</u>
3. lower   8. nice   13. <u>money</u>
4. <u>does</u>   9. read   14. <u>of</u>
5. change 10. <u>other</u>

1. <u>dis</u>honest   d
2. <u>dis</u>armed   c
3. <u>dis</u>continued   f
4. <u>dis</u>agreement   b
5. <u>dis</u>like   a
6. <u>dis</u>courage   g
7. <u>dis</u>ability   e

1. disarmed
2. disagreement
3. discontinued
4. dislike
5. disability

Page 101

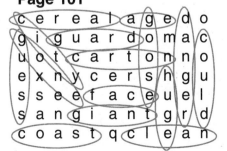

These words should be marked.
Correct spelling is underlined.
2. cartun   <u>carton</u>
3. sereal   <u>cereal</u>
4. citee   <u>city</u>
6. koast   coast
8. danjer   <u>danger</u>
9. fase   <u>face</u>
11. gawn   <u>gone</u>
13. gard   <u>guard</u>
15. huje   <u>huge</u>

Page 102
Pictures will vary but
must reflect the meaning
of the phrase.

1. guard
2. City
3. Danger
4. guess   age
5. clean
6. giant

Page 103
s	k	j	g
cereal	carton	age	gone
city	clean	danger	goose
face	coast	giant	guard
	could	huge	guess

1. guess   3. huge   5. gone
2. city   4. danger 6. clean

1. danger   safety
2. know   guess
3. tiny   huge
4. present   gone

Page 105
1. word   6. were   11. first
2. work   7. nurse   12. wear
3. girl   8. bird   13. turned
4. learn   9. world   14. stirred
5. fire   10. jury   15. here

These words should be marked.
Correct spellings are underlined.
wurk	<u>work</u>
tirned	<u>turned</u>
frie	<u>fire</u>
ferst	<u>first</u>
herd	<u>heard</u>
gril	<u>girl</u>
nerse	<u>nurse</u>
gerl	<u>girl</u>
lurn	<u>learn</u>
nurs	<u>nurse</u>

Page 106
1. nurse
2. world
   here
   stirred
3. word
4. jury
5. b
6. first
   work
   girl
   here
Sentences will vary.

Page 107
1. first
2. learn
3. turned
4. girl
5. word
6. were
7. faster
8. work

1. n<u>ur</u>se
2. b<u>ir</u>d
3. h<u>er</u>
4. w<u>or</u>ld
5. l<u>ear</u>n
6. quick<u>er</u>
7. w<u>or</u>d
8. st<u>ir</u>red

1. wear   4. first   7. word
2. were   5. girl   8. fire
3. work   6. learn 9. nurse

1. wear
2. were
3. work
4. nurse

Page 109
1. far — th
2. lar — n't
3. nor — m
4. are — re
5. sta — ge
6. warn — fore
7. be — ner
8. part — ing

1. farm
2. large
3. north
4. aren't
5. stare
6. warning
7. before
8. partner

These words should be marked.
Correct spellings are underlined.
  1. arent   <u>aren't</u>
  3. mor   <u>more</u>
  4. chard   <u>chart</u>
  6. narth   <u>north</u>
  7. stayr   <u>stare</u>
  9. befor   <u>before</u>
 12. partnur   <u>partner</u>
 15. larje   <u>large</u>

Page 110
1. partner before
2. large farm
3. start morning
4. warning chart
5. Aren't care horse
6. stare
7. hard
Sentences will vary.

Page 111
1. p<u>ar</u>tner 6. <u>ar</u>en't 11. m<u>or</u>e
2. n<u>or</u>th 7. bef<u>or</u>e 12. ch<u>ar</u>t
3. m<u>or</u>ning 8. w<u>ar</u>ning 13. st<u>ar</u>t
4. c<u>ar</u>e 9. st<u>ar</u>e 14. h<u>or</u>se
5. h<u>ar</u>d 10. l<u>ar</u>ge 15. f<u>ar</u>m

1. hard
2. large
3. more
4. before
5. north
6. morning
7. start

1. large tiny
2. morning evening
3. south north
4. before after

Page 113
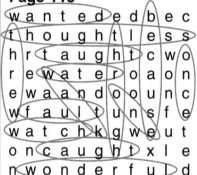

These words should be marked.
Correct spellings are underlined.
  1. wundir   <u>wonder</u>
  3. walck   <u>walk</u>
  4. wunce   <u>once</u>
  5. becuz   <u>because</u>
  6. tawght   <u>taught</u>
  8. watur   <u>water</u>
 10. fawlt   <u>fault</u>
 12. throo   <u>threw/through</u>
 13. wach   <u>watch</u>
 14. onederful <u>wonderful</u>

Page 114
1. through
   threw
2. caught   taught
   threw   through
3. a
4. once
5. wonderful
6. catch   <u>caught</u>
   teach   <u>taught</u>
   throw   <u>threw</u>
   want   <u>wanted</u>
Sentences will vary.

Page 115
wu in **won**   **wa** in **wall**
one   wanted
wonderful   water
wonder   watch
once   walk

aw in **fawn**   **oo** in **too**
thought   threw
because   through
caught
fault
taught

1. wonderful
2. thoughtless
3. thoughtful
4. joyful
5. helpless
6. helpful

Page 117
1. co — y
2. calen — ber
3. part — lor
4. ev — dar
5. num — ery
6. o — gar
7. doc — dor
8. for — tor
9. su — ty
10. weath — ter
11. li — ter
12. bet — ar
13. af — er

1. color
2. calendar
3. party
4. every
5. number
6. odor
7. doctor
8. forty
9. sugar
10. weather
11. liar
12. better
13. after

These words should be marked.
Correct spellings are underlined.
1. calender   doller
   <u>calendar</u>   <u>dollar</u>
2. partie   fourty
   <u>party</u>   <u>forty</u>
3. bettir   doctur
   <u>better</u>   <u>doctor</u>
4. nummer   <u>number</u>
5. Evry oder
   <u>Every</u> <u>odor</u>

Page 118
1. liar <u>ar</u> after <u>er</u> doctor <u>or</u>
2. long e
3. doctor
4. liar
5. A calendar tells the date.
6. sugar
7. every
8. before <u>after</u>
   worse <u>better</u>
Sentences will vary.

Page 119
color   every   better
odor   calendar   sugar
dollar   watch   stare
march   number   liar
store   weather   after

1. co lor   7. par ty
2. cal en dar   8. li ar
3. bet ter   9. weath er
4. eve ry   10. o dor
5. store   11. af ter
6. num ber   12. su gar

Page 121
1. Fri   phan
2. fa   ew
3. or   day
4. neph   nough
5. e   ther
6. pho   pi   py
7. al   hap   bet
8. un   to   graph
9. hap   pha   ly

1. Friday   6. photograph
2. father   7. alphabet
3. orphan   8. unhappy
4. nephew   9. happily
5. enough

These words should be marked.
Correct spellings are underlined.
1. fone   <u>phone</u>
2. haf   <u>half</u>
3. alfabet   <u>alphabet</u>
5. fotograph   <u>photograph</u>
6. fadder   <u>father</u>
7. nefew   <u>nephew</u>
9. orfan   <u>orphan</u>
11. enuf   <u>enough</u>
12. Fritay   <u>Friday</u>

Page 122
1. photograph
2. orphan
3. alphabet
4. enough
5. cough
6. father nephew
7. enough stuff
8. photograph alphabet
Sentences will vary.

Page 123
1. <u>phone</u>
2. enou<u>gh</u>
3. or<u>ph</u>an
4. <u>f</u>ather
5. <u>F</u>riday
6. ne<u>ph</u>ew
7. hal<u>f</u>
8. gra<u>ph</u>
9. al<u>ph</u>abet
10. <u>ph</u>otogra<u>ph</u>

1. photograph
2. alphabet
3. half Father

1. slowly carefully
2. darkness
3. happily
4. kindness happiness

Page 125
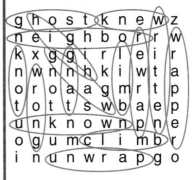

These words should be marked.
Correct spellings are underlined.
gost   <u>ghost</u>
naybor   <u>neighbor</u>
hi   <u>high</u>
knoo   <u>know</u>
unknone   <u>unknown</u>
rong   <u>wrong</u>
enwrap   <u>unwrap</u>
clim   <u>climb</u>
naw   <u>gnaw</u>

1. not   <u>knot</u>
2. nats   <u>gnats</u>
3. lim   <u>limb</u>

Page 126
Across   Down
1. unknown   2. neighbor
4. climb   3. wrong
6. unwrap   5. written
8. ghost   7. gnat
9. knot   8. gnaw

Page 127
ghost   knew   wrong
high   write   unwrap
gnaw   knot   climb
limb   unknown gnat

1. rewrap
2. unknown
3. unsure
4. rewrite
5. Unwrap
6. repaint

Page 129
1. use<u>ful</u>   5. smart<u>er</u>   9. care<u>ful</u>
2. use<u>less</u>   6. slow<u>ly</u>   10. care<u>less</u>
3. quiet<u>ly</u>   7. joy<u>ful</u>   11. fear<u>ful</u>
4. worth<u>less</u>   8. fast<u>er</u>   12. fear<u>less</u>

These words should be marked.
Correct spellings are underlined.
1. slooly kwietly <u>slowly</u> <u>quietly</u>
2. joyfull fastist <u>joyful</u> <u>fastest</u>
3. useles kareless
   <u>useless</u> <u>careless</u>
4. happyest <u>happiest</u>
5. feerless quikly
   <u>fearless</u> <u>quickly</u>

Page 130
1. b
2. c
3. quickly   <u>slowly</u>
   useful   <u>useless</u>
   careless   <u>careful</u>
   saddest   <u>happiest</u>
4. fearful
5. careless
Sentences will vary.

Page 131
1. fastest - no change
2. happiest - y to i, add est
3. quickest - no change
4. funniest - y to i, add est
5. saddest - double consonant
6. biggest - double consonant
7. smartest - no change
8. silliest - y to i, add est

1. care<u>ful</u> care<u>less</u>
2. fear<u>less</u> fear<u>ful</u>
3. use<u>less</u> use<u>ful</u>

1. fast<u>er</u> fast<u>est</u>
2. slow<u>er</u> slow<u>est</u>
3. hard<u>est</u> hard<u>er</u>

Page 133

These words should be marked.
Correct spellings are underlined.
1. muther bruther   <u>mother</u> <u>brother</u>
2. hurd frend   <u>heard</u> <u>friend</u>
3. herd feeld   <u>heard</u> <u>field</u>

4. Erly yeer   <u>Early</u> <u>year</u>
5. eta unother   <u>eat</u> <u>another</u>

Page 134
Across
3. brother
4. eat
6. measure
7. heard
8. year
10. field
11. mother

Down
1. shield
2. friend
3. break
4. early
5. turned
7. head
9. near

Page 135

long e	long a	short e	schwa
eat	break	head	another
field		measure	brother
shield			mother
near			
year			

Answers will vary, but may include:

__other	_eat
mother	beat
brother	seat
another	neat
smother	wheat

_ead	_ear
read	hear
dead	near
lead	year
thread	fear

Page 137
1. raw
2. drow
3. threi
4. heret
5. ightn
6. ritwe
7. twai
8. peice
9. rou
10. hrou
11. ritgh
12. rwote

their
word
there
war
write
night
right
wait
piece
wrote
hour
our

These words should be marked.
Correct spellings are underlined.
1. rite their   <u>right</u> <u>there</u>
2. night nite   <u>knight</u> <u>night</u>
3. weight howr   <u>wait</u> <u>hour</u>
4. Hour nitgh   <u>Our</u> <u>night</u>
5. peace there   <u>piece</u> <u>their</u>
6. right werd   <u>write</u> <u>word</u>

Page 138
1. their   there
2. knight's   night
3. write   right
4. hour   our
5. weight
6. piece   peace
7. wrote
Sentences will vary.

Page 139

long a	long i	long e
weight	night	piece
wait	knight	flee
plain	write	peace
plane	right	beach
stair	sight	flea
stare	site	beech

1. write
2. night
3. there
4. right
5. peace
6. wait
7. piece
8. our

1. write   erase
2. wait   leave
3. peace   war

Page 141
1. a
2. un
3. pre
4. peo
5. min
6. beau
7. va
8. re
9. al
10. hos

sents
ute
gainst
til
ple
ca
read
ti
pit
mem

ber
ful
al
y
tion

1. against
2. until
3. presents
4. people
5. minute
6. beautiful
7. vacation
8. remember
9. already
10. hospital